RISING ★ STARS

MEDAL MATHS

Year 6

Practice and Homework Book

By
Richard Cooper

```
Medal Maths Practice and
   Homework Book Year 6

This is not a photocopiable book.
```

Rising Stars UK Ltd., 22 Grafton Street, London W1S 4EX
www.risingstars-uk.com

All facts are correct at time of going to press.

Published 2004
Reprinted 2005, 2006, 2007
Text, design and layout © Rising Stars UK Ltd.

Editorial: Tanya Solomons
Concept design: Marc Burville-Riley
Design: Clive Sutherland
Illustrations: © Clive Sutherland and Marc Burville-Riley
Cover design: Marc Burville-Riley

British Library Cataloguing in Publication Data
A CIP record for this book is available from the British Library.

ISBN 978 1 904591 43 6

Printed by Cromwell Press, Wiltshire, UK.

Contents

How to use this book

Medal Maths has been created to provide pupils with a complete series of questions to support the whole National Numeracy Strategy Framework. There are three different levels of questions: Bronze, Silver and Gold.

Answers are available in the Medal Maths Teacher's Book Year 6.

Explanations
Explanations and examples are given for each objective to support children working independently.

Pupil's Notes

Practice and more practice is the best method for getting results and improving your performance in Maths.

For the best results:

a) Read the explanation.

b) Complete the questions at the most appropriate level.

c) Use the hints and tips to help you.

d) See if you can complete the next level of questions!

Bronze Medal Questions
These questions are an ideal starting point. They support the work covered in the Silver questions.

Silver Medal Questions
These questions are set at the expected level for Year 6 as presented by the NNS Framework.

How to use this book

National Numeracy Strategy
Every area of the NNS is covered (including all the Mental Maths objectives).

Objective
Each objective is covered through an explanation, three levels of questions and hints and tips.

---

6 Numbers and the number system

Estimating

Estimating means 'a clever guess'. Being able to estimate an answer is very useful in maths. If you can estimate, you can use the skill to check your answers to see if they are sensible.

Bronze

a) Estimate how many:
1. 10p coins will make a straight line 1 metre long
2. Teachers are in your school
3. Classrooms are in your school
4. Cars will make a straight line 100m long
5. Pages are in this book

b) Estimate the position of the arrows on these lines:
1. 0 — 1000
2. 0 — 100
3. 0 — 200
4. 0 — 10
5. 0 — 1000

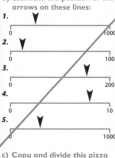

c) Copy and divide this pizza into equal portions for:
1. 3 people
2. 5 people
3. 8 people
4. 12 people
5. 2 people

Silver

a) Estimate how many:
1. 10p coins will make a straight line 1km long
2. Children are in your school
3. Doors are in your school
4. Odd pages there are in this book
5. Questions are in this book

b) Estimate the position of the arrows on these lines:
1. 0 — 100
2. 0 — 100
3. 0 — 100
4. 0 — 100
5. 0 — 100

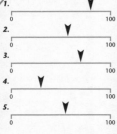

c) Estimate the fraction of the cakes that has been eaten:
1.   2.
3.   4.

Gold

a) Estimate how many:
1. Days you have been alive
2. Windows there are in your school
3. Smarties in a tube
4. Questions there are in this book
5. Leaves there are on a tree

b) Estimate the position of the arrows on these lines:
1. 0 — 1250
2. 0 — 2500
3. 0 — 3000
4. 0 — 15000
5. −150 — 150

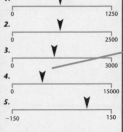

c) Estimate the fraction of each shape that has been shaded:
1.   2.
3.   4.

Gold Medal Questions
These questions are a bit harder. They extend the work of the Silver questions.

Questions
There are more than 2500 questions covering all the NNS Objectives.

Training Tips

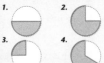 Make sure you can read, write and spell correctly these words and phrases – *guess, estimate, approximate, roughly, nearly, too many, too few.*
Picture your estimates in your mind – do they look sensible?

Sport Theme
The sport theme is often used within the questions to put the maths into context.

Hints and Tips
Hints and tips support lower ability students and help to consolidate learning.

Estimating

Estimating means 'a clever guess'. Being able to estimate an answer is very useful in maths. If you can estimate, you can use the skill to check your answers to see if they are sensible.

 Bronze

a) Estimate how many:

1. 10p coins will make a straight line 1 metre long
2. Teachers are in your school
3. Classrooms are in your school
4. Cars will make a straight line 100 m long
5. Pages are in this book

b) Estimate the position of the arrows on these lines:

1.

0   1000

2.

0   100

3.

0   200

4.

0   10

5.

0   1000

c) Copy and divide this pizza into equal portions for:

1. 3 people
2. 5 people
3. 8 people
4. 12 people
5. 2 people

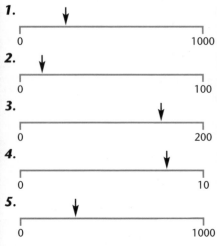

 Silver

a) Estimate how many:

1. 10p coins will make a straight line 1km long
2. Children are in your school
3. Doors are in your school
4. Odd pages there are in this book
5. Questions are in this book

b) Estimate the position of the arrows on these lines:

1.

0   100

2.

0   100

3.

0   100

4.

0   100

5.

0   100

c) Estimate the fraction of the cakes that has been eaten:

1.   2.

3.   4.

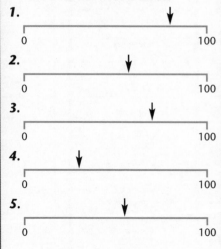

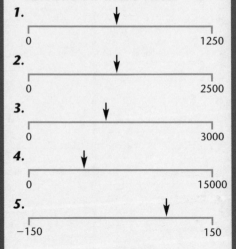

Gold

a) Estimate how many:

1. Days you have been alive
2. Windows there are in your school
3. Smarties in a tube
4. Questions there are in this book
5. Leaves there are on a tree

b) Estimate the position of the arrows on these lines:

1.

0   1250

2.

0   2500

3.

0   3000

4.

0   15000

5.

−150   150

c) Estimate the fraction of each shape that has been shaded:

1.   2.

3.   4.

 **Training Tips**

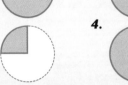 **Make sure you can read, write and spell correctly these words and phrases –**
guess, estimate, approximate, roughly, nearly, too many, too few.
Picture your estimates in your mind – do they look sensible?

Rounding

Rounding whole numbers to the nearest 10, 100 or 1000 can be a useful way of doing calculations.

> *Example*
> 716 + 397 = ? This is roughly 700 + 400 which is 1100.
> You now know that the answer is going to be around 1100.
> 716 + 397 = 1113. That is close to 1100.

Bronze

a) **Round these numbers to the nearest hundred:**

1. 672   2. 235

3. 983   4. 768

5. 5490   6. 4444

7. 3901   8. 8550

9. 420   10. 1381

b) **Round these distances from London to the nearest 100 miles:**

1. **Paris**   215 miles

2. **Milan**   609 miles

3. **Brussels**   217 miles

4. **Dublin**   279 miles

5. **New York**   3440 miles

c) **Approximate these sums:**

1. 18 x 31

2. 29 x 42

3. 9 x 51

4. 38 x 11

5. 8 x 22

Silver

a) **Would you estimate these numbers to the nearest 10, 100, 1000, 10 000 or 1 000 000?**

1. The number of people on a full bus

2. The number of people who live in France

3. Spectators at Millennium Stadium, Cardiff

4. Children in your class

5. Children in your school

6. The number of miles to the moon

7. The number of mobile phones in the United Kingdom

8. The number of days in 3 years

b) **Approximate these calculations:**

1. 8.16 × 7.83

2. 5.01 − 2.82

3. 6.65 + 4.22

4. 15.3 × 19.2

5. 10.10 × 19.91

6. 8.71 + 12.68

7. 1.95 + 29.7

8. 17.4 − 13.5

Gold

a) **Round these numbers to the nearest 1000:**

1. 9784

2. 8054

3. 2220

4. 1920

5. 16 439

6. 14 967

7. 29 305

8. 39 909

b) **Approximate the answers to these calculations:**

1. (5033 − 486) ÷ 150 =

2. (8445 − 3112) ÷ 55 =

3. (1.3 × 34.5) + (1.5 × 20.6) =

4. 408 + (168 + 203) =

5. (4532 − 1395) + 8390 =

6. (1604 + 7021) × 9 =

7. (1.25 × 30.5) − 8.97 =

8. 425 + 308 + 693 =

 Training Tips

 Remember, we always round 5 or more up, e.g. 9500 rounds up to 10 000.

Use rounding to mentally check the answers to your calculations.

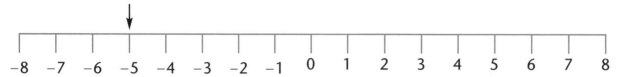

Negative numbers

Negative numbers are numbers below zero. This arrow is pointing to negative 5 or minus 5.

| −8 | −7 | −6 | −5 | −4 | −3 | −2 | −1 | 0 | 1 | 2 | 3 | 4 | 5 | 6 | 7 | 8 |

Bronze

F A B DH E G C
−5 −4 −3 −2 −1 0 1 2 3 4 5

a) What number is each arrow pointing to?

1. A   **2.** B   **3.** C   **4.** D
5. E   **6.** F   **7.** G   **8.** H

b) Put these negative numbers in order, smallest first:

1. −4 −7 −1 −5 −8
2. −12 −6 −15 −9 −21
3. −1 −8 −18 −12 −10
4. −3 −5 −9 −2 −4
5. −22 −12 −33 −34 −32

c) Look at this thermometer. Use it to answer these questions:

1. The thermometer says − 3 degrees. It then rises by 8 degrees. What is the final reading?

2. The temperature falls from 7 °C to −3 °C. How many degrees does the temperature fall?

3. If the temperature in the evening is 5 °C, how far must it fall to reach −2 °C?

4. The temperature rises to 6 °C from −1 °C in the morning. How far is this?

(Thermometer scale: 8, 7, 6, 5, 4, 3, 2, 1, 0, −1, −2, −3)

Silver

a) Put these numbers in order – lowest first:

1. −42, 6, 29, −45, −6
2. −35, −22, −56, −2, −44
3. 18, −9, −2, 12, −5
4. −22, −1, −19, −10, −9
5. 1, 0, −1, 2, −2
6. −2, −4, −3, 5, 0
7. 16, 61, −6, −16, 15
8. 2, 3, 7, −1, −6
9. 101, −10, 1, −1, 11
10. 5, −6, 7, −3, 0

b) Jamie is watching his football team's performance in the league. He writes down the move in places in the table each week. His team starts in 2nd place.

	Week 1	Week 2	Week 3	Week 4	Week 5	Week 6
2nd place		−1	+2	0	−3	+1

1. What was his team's highest place?

2. Which week did this happen?

3. In which week did they make the biggest jump up?

4. Where did the team finish after 6 weeks?

5. How many weeks did the team not move?

Gold

a) Solve these problems:

1. −12 + ☐ = 4
2. −5 + ☐ = 0
3. −5 + ☐ = −3
4. −4 + ☐ = 5
5. −11 + ☐ = −8
6. −3 + 2 = ☐
7. 1 − 5 = ☐
8. 14 − 19 = ☐
9. −4 − 2 = ☐
10. −15 + 17 = ☐

b) In golf, the lower the score, the better. These are Tim's scores in 8 rounds of golf:

Round 1	−2	Round 5	−5
Round 2	3	Round 6	−3
Round 3	4	Round 7	1
Round 4	0	Round 8	−2

Answer these questions about Tim's golf game:

1. What was his lowest score?

2. What was his highest score?

3. What was his mean score?

4. How much better was his 4th round than his 3rd round?

5. Which game showed the best improvement on the previous game?

Training Tips

Picture negative numbers as rungs on a ladder or steps up and down.

When counting up and down scales or number lines, don't forget to include the zero.

Number sequences

Being able to recognise patterns and sequences in numbers can very useful.

Question: The Olympic Games are held every four years.
When will the next three Olympics be held after 2004?

Answer: 2008, 2012 and 2016 – you just count on 4 years each time.

Bronze

a) **Fill in the missing numbers in these sequences:**

1. 24, ☐, 46, 57, ☐

2. 3, 6, 9, ☐, ☐

3. 6, ☐, 18, ☐, 30

4. 30, ☐, ☐, 60, 70

5. 5, 8, ☐, 14, ☐

6. 145, 120, 95, ☐, ☐

7. 8, ☐, 50, ☐, 92

8. 8, 12, ☐, ☐ 24

b) **Fill in the missing numbers in these sequences:**

1. 55, 66, ☐, ☐, 99, 110

2. 90, 75, 60, ☐, ☐

3. 12, 56, ☐, 144, ☐

4. −3, −8, ☐, ☐, −23

5. 14, ☐, 28, ☐, 42

6. 2, 21, ☐, ☐, 78

7. 36, 18, 0, ☐, ☐

8. ☐, ☐, 70, 61, 52

Silver

a) **Fill in the missing numbers in these sequences:**

1. 15, 30, ☐, ☐, 75

2. 26, 34, 42, ☐, ☐

3. 47, 56, ☐, ☐, 83

4. 88, 94, ☐, 106, ☐

5. 121, ☐, 135, 142, ☐

6. 204, 226, ☐, ☐, 292

7. ☐, 57, ☐, 71, ☐

8. 121, 222, ☐, 424, ☐

b) **Fill in the missing numbers in these sequences:**

1. 400, 350, ☐, ☐, 200

2. 63, 57, ☐, ☐, 39

3. 108, ☐, ☐, 75, 64

4. 325, 299, ☐, 247, ☐

5. 72, 61, ☐, 39, 28, ☐

6. −18, −14, ☐, −6, ☐

7. −26, ☐, −10, ☐, 6

8. −33, −22, ☐, ☐, 11

Gold

Halley's Comet appears every 76 years. The last appearance was in 1986.

a) Write down the year of the next 10 appearences of Halley's comet.

b) Write down the years of the previous 10 visits of Halley's Comet.

Training Tips

When studying sequences, try to find the differences between the numbers you are given.

Always test your predictions before giving an answer – do they work?

Properties of numbers

A whole number can be divided by:

3 ⟶ if the sum of its digits is divisible by 3
6 ⟶ if it is even and is also divisible by 3
8 ⟶ if half of it is divisible by 4
9 ⟶ if the sum of its digits is divisible by 9
25 ⟶ if the last two digits are 00, 25, 50 or 75

Bronze

a) **Which numbers in these sets can be divided exactly by 7?**
1. 5, 19, 21, 25, 32, 42
2. 2, 14, 15, 34, 39, 44
3. 6, 16, 28, 34, 46, 56
4. 84, 93, 102, 107, 121

b) **Which numbers in these sets can be divided exactly by 8?**
1. 7, 16, 23, 32, 36, 39
2. 9, 22, 35, 40, 53, 62
3. 17, 26, 37, 47, 48
4. 64, 79, 82, 88, 93

c) **Which of these numbers can be divided exactly by 2 or 3?**
1. 3, 6, 5, 1, 8, 7
2. 25, 18, 27, 6, 45, 61
3. 89, 45, 34, 36, 11, 78
4. 53, 32, 18, 57, 17, 19

d) **Which of these numbers can be divided exactly by 4 or 5?**
1. 6, 8, 5, 13, 20, 23
2. 29, 37, 40, 46, 52, 58
3. 81, 92, 95, 100, 106, 110
4. 80, 94, 98, 102, 104, 105

Silver

a) **Which numbers in these sets are divisible by 12?**
1. 24, 39, 44, 60, 71, 93
2. 30, 36, 46, 56, 76, 80
3. 38, 48, 59, 72, 88, 99
4. 144, 288, 377, 466, 500

b) **Which numbers are divisible by 15?**
1. 45, 76, 94, 105, 143, 201
2. 145, 160, 165, 170, 175, 200
3. 55, 74, 85, 115, 150, 168
4. 250, 350, 450, 550, 650, 750

c) **Find the smallest number that is a common multiple of the following two numbers:**
1. 6 and 10
2. 8 and 12
3. 12 and 16
4. 6 and 15
5. 8 and 20
6. 2 and 10
7. 5 and 20
8. 6 and 8

Gold

a) **Which numbers in these sets are divisible by 45?**
1. 175, 180, 367, 734, 765
2. 90, 122, 175, 245, 313, 405
3. 60, 135, 200, 270, 358, 389
4. 1026, 1035, 1127, 1150, 1207, 1222

b) **Which numbers in these sets are divisible by 115?**
1. 690, 768, 843, 2760, 5261
2. 451, 500, 505, 575, 595, 600
3. 460, 577, 688, 909, 1035, 1200
4. 2200, 2300, 2400, 2500, 2600, 2700

c) **Find the smallest number that is a common multiple of the following two numbers:**
1. 25 and 30
2. 30 and 35
3. 12 and 18
4. 15 and 20
5. 35 and 40
6. 40 and 50
7. 60 and 11
8. 3, 9 and 21

Training Tips

A multiple is the answer when you multiply any number by a whole number.
35 is a multiple of 7 and 5 and of 1 and 35.

Square numbers

36 · 81 · 16 · 25 · 64

Square numbers
Square numbers are numbers that are the product of a number being multiplied by itself.

Example

36 is a square number because $6 \times 6 = 36$.
We say that 6^2 is 'six squared' so 6^2 is 36.

Bronze

a) Write these down in words.

1. 2^2 **2.** 5^2 **3.** 7^2

4. 8^2 **5.** 10^2

b) Try these questions

1. What is 5 squared?

2. What is 9 squared?

3. What is 8 squared?

4. What is 10 squared?

5. What is 3 squared?

c) Which of these are square numbers?

1. 2 3 1 5 7

2. 5 4 6 8 10

3. 7 8 9 10 11

4. 10 12 14 16 18

5. 20 25 30 35 40

Silver

**a) Answer these questions
What is:**

1. 12^2 **2.** 15^2 **3.** 17^2

4. 14^2 **5.** 20^2 **6.** 36^2

7. 13^2 **8.** 41^2

b) Use a calculator for these:

1. What number, when multiplied by itself, gives 1225.

2. Find two consecutive numbers with a product of 4160.

3. The area of a square is 676 cm squared. What is the length of its sides?

4. 7744 is what number squared?

5. A square has an area of 1764 cm squared. What is the length of its sides?

6. What number squared is closest to 2000?

7. 289 is the product of what number squared?

8. What number, when multiplied by itself, gives 4356.

Gold

a) What is:

1. 100^2 **2.** 89^2 **3.** 72^2

4. 64^2 **5.** 33^2 **6.** 17^2

7. 28^2 **8.** 99^2

b) Try these:

1. What number, when multiplied by itself, gives 11 664.

2. A square is 14 641 cm squared. What length are the sides?

3. 12 769 is the product of what number squared?

4. 101 squared is what?

5. 41 616 is what squared?

6. A square is 66 049 cm squared. What length are the sides?

7. 96 721 is the square. What number is multiplied by itself?

8. What number, when multiplied by itself, gives 17 956

Training Tips

Try to relate square numbers to drawings of squares.

Learn all the square numbers up to 12×12 (1, 2, 4, 9, 16, 25, 36, 49, 64, 81, 100, 121, 144).

Factors and prime numbers

Factors
The pairs of factors for the number 18 are: 1 and 18, 2 and 9, 3 and 6

Prime numbers
A prime number is a number greater than 1 that only has two factors
– itself and 1.

The first 10 prime numbers are 2, 3, 5, 7, 11, 13, 17, 19, 23 and 29

Bronze

What are the pairs of factors for these numbers?

1. 36
2. 44
3. 56
4. 24
5. 51
6. 99
7. 34
8. 64
9. 72
10. 80
11. 33
12. 42
13. 81
14. 19
15. 27

Silver

a) Which of these are prime numbers?

1. 27, 29, 32, 33, 34
2. 30, 31, 32, 33, 34
3. 34, 35, 36, 37, 38
4. 85, 86, 87, 88, 89
5. 60, 61, 62, 63, 64
6. 40, 41, 42, 43, 44
7. 71, 72, 73, 74, 75
8. 96, 97, 98, 99, 100
9. 14, 25, 33, 43, 55
10. 55, 56, 57, 58, 59
11. 11, 12, 14, 16, 21
12. 21, 51, 71, 81, 91
13. 23, 33, 63, 93, 39

b) Which of these aren't prime numbers?

1. 17, 71, 13, 31, 16, 61
2. 79, 97, 11, 98, 89

Gold

Write down the next 20 Prime numbers after 100.

Training Tips

    Prime numbers are always odd, with the exception of the number 2.

    The largest known prime number has over six million digits!

Fractions

Simplifying fractions

The fraction $\frac{4}{16}$, can be cancelled down to $\frac{1}{4}$ by dividing the numerator and the denominator by the same number – in this case 4.

Mixed numbers

The improper fraction $\frac{163}{10}$ is $16\frac{3}{10}$ when changed to a mixed number.

1															
$\frac{1}{2}$								$\frac{1}{2}$							
$\frac{1}{3}$					$\frac{1}{3}$					$\frac{1}{3}$					
$\frac{1}{4}$				$\frac{1}{4}$				$\frac{1}{4}$				$\frac{1}{4}$			
$\frac{1}{5}$			$\frac{1}{5}$			$\frac{1}{5}$			$\frac{1}{5}$			$\frac{1}{5}$			
$\frac{1}{6}$		$\frac{1}{6}$		$\frac{1}{6}$		$\frac{1}{6}$		$\frac{1}{6}$		$\frac{1}{6}$					
$\frac{1}{8}$	$\frac{1}{8}$	$\frac{1}{8}$	$\frac{1}{8}$	$\frac{1}{8}$	$\frac{1}{8}$	$\frac{1}{8}$	$\frac{1}{8}$								
$\frac{1}{10}$	$\frac{1}{10}$	$\frac{1}{10}$	$\frac{1}{10}$	$\frac{1}{10}$	$\frac{1}{10}$	$\frac{1}{10}$	$\frac{1}{10}$	$\frac{1}{10}$	$\frac{1}{10}$						
$\frac{1}{12}$	$\frac{1}{12}$	$\frac{1}{12}$	$\frac{1}{12}$	$\frac{1}{12}$	$\frac{1}{12}$	$\frac{1}{12}$	$\frac{1}{12}$	$\frac{1}{12}$	$\frac{1}{12}$	$\frac{1}{12}$	$\frac{1}{12}$				
$\frac{1}{16}$	$\frac{1}{16}$	$\frac{1}{16}$	$\frac{1}{16}$	$\frac{1}{16}$	$\frac{1}{16}$	$\frac{1}{16}$	$\frac{1}{16}$	$\frac{1}{16}$	$\frac{1}{16}$	$\frac{1}{16}$	$\frac{1}{16}$	$\frac{1}{16}$	$\frac{1}{16}$	$\frac{1}{16}$	$\frac{1}{16}$

Bronze

Look at the fraction wall above. One quarter is half of one half.

a) Complete these sentences:

2. Two sixths is the same as?
2. Two eights is the same as?
3. Four tenths is the same as?
4. Nine twelfths is the same as?
5. Twelve sixteenths is the same as?
6. Four quarters is the same as?
7. One sixth is half of?
8. One eighth is half of?

b) Place these in order – smallest first:

1. $\frac{3}{5}, \frac{3}{6}, \frac{3}{8}, \frac{4}{9}, \frac{2}{5}$
2. $\frac{6}{9}, \frac{6}{10}, \frac{5}{8}, \frac{5}{9}, \frac{4}{5}$
3. $1\frac{3}{5}, 1\frac{5}{6}, 1\frac{5}{8}, 1\frac{6}{9}, 1\frac{3}{4}$
4. $\frac{3}{5}, \frac{4}{6}, \frac{7}{9}, \frac{9}{10}, \frac{8}{9}$
5. $1\frac{1}{2}, \frac{3}{4}, 1\frac{1}{4}, 2, \frac{1}{2}$
6. $\frac{1}{12}, \frac{2}{5}, \frac{3}{4}, 1, \frac{4}{16}$
7. $1\frac{1}{2}, \frac{5}{6}, 1\frac{8}{12}, 2\frac{1}{12}, \frac{9}{10}$
8. $1\frac{1}{12}, 1\frac{1}{10}, 1\frac{1}{16}, 1\frac{1}{5}, 1\frac{1}{8}$

Silver

a) Simplify these fractions to their lowest form:

1. $\frac{4}{12}$
2. $\frac{5}{25}$
3. $\frac{6}{12}$
4. $\frac{4}{16}$
5. $\frac{8}{12}$
6. $\frac{10}{16}$
7. $\frac{5}{10}$
8. $\frac{15}{20}$

b) Simplify these fractions and then order them smallest to biggest:

1. $2\frac{3}{10}, 1\frac{1}{2}, 2\frac{3}{4}, 2\frac{1}{10}$
2. $\frac{8}{12}, \frac{8}{16}, \frac{8}{10}, \frac{8}{9}$
3. $\frac{4}{6}, \frac{2}{5}, \frac{5}{10}, \frac{6}{9}$
4. $1\frac{2}{10}, 1\frac{2}{6}, 1\frac{4}{12}, 1\frac{6}{16}$
5. $3\frac{2}{6}, 2\frac{14}{16}, 3\frac{4}{8}, 4\frac{6}{9}$
6. $\frac{9}{10}, \frac{9}{12}, \frac{9}{16}, \frac{9}{18}$
7. $4\frac{1}{2}, 4\frac{4}{12}, 4\frac{8}{12}, 4\frac{10}{12}$
8. $\frac{8}{12}, \frac{3}{6}, \frac{4}{10}, \frac{5}{15}$

Gold

a) Simplify these fractions to their lowest form:

1. $\frac{36}{60}$
2. $\frac{49}{77}$
3. $\frac{55}{105}$
4. $\frac{56}{72}$
5. $\frac{9}{81}$
6. $\frac{27}{90}$
7. $\frac{32}{96}$
8. $\frac{12}{120}$

b) Convert these improper fractions to mixed numbers:

1. $\frac{145}{12}$
2. $\frac{54}{13}$
3. $\frac{123}{25}$
4. $\frac{118}{34}$
5. $\frac{189}{21}$
6. $\frac{101}{7}$
7. $\frac{267}{14}$
8. $\frac{150}{45}$

Training Tips

 Learn as many fraction equivalents as you can. (e.g. $\frac{1}{3} = \frac{2}{6} = \frac{3}{9} = \frac{4}{12} = \frac{5}{15}$)

 Start to picture fractions in your head. Imagine how you could divide the cover of this book into 4 equal parts.

Finding fractions of numbers and quantities

Finding a fifth of something is the same as dividing it by 5. For example to find a fifth of 15 we divide 15 by 5 to give the answer 3.

So, a $\frac{1}{5}$ of 15 is the same as 15 divided by 5.

Bronze

Find these fractions and amounts:

1. What is one tenth of 180?

2. What is $\frac{1}{4}$ of 80?

3. What is $\frac{3}{10}$ of 50?

4. What is $\frac{7}{10}$ of 250?

5. What is $\frac{4}{5}$ of 100?

6. What is $\frac{1}{10}$ of 1000?

7. What is $\frac{2}{3}$ of 99?

8. What is one quarter of 72?

9. What fraction of one week is 2 days?

10. What fraction of 1 l is 235 ml?

11. What fraction of 1 km is 250 m?

12. What fraction of 1 metre is 40 cm?

13. What fraction of 1 kg is 200 g?

14. What fraction of one day is 3 hours?

15. What fraction of £1 is 20p?

16. What fraction of 20p is 5p?

Silver

Find these fractions and amounts:

1. What is $\frac{7}{10}$ of 200?

2. What is $\frac{4}{5}$ of 45?

3. What is $\frac{5}{6}$ of 66?

4. What fraction of 1 metre is 65 cm?

5. What fraction of 1 kg is 483 g?

6. What fraction of one year is one week?

7. What is $\frac{3}{8}$ of 64?

8. What is $\frac{7}{9}$ of 81?

9. What is $\frac{24}{25}$ of 250?

10. What fraction of £5 is £1.25?

11. What fraction of £10 is £3.50?

12. What fraction of 1 km is 850 m?

13. What is $\frac{1}{8}$ of 96?

14. What is $\frac{7}{12}$ of 144?

15. What is a quarter of 404?

16. What is $\frac{2}{7}$ of 91?

Gold

Find these fractions and amounts:

1. How many fifths in $24\frac{3}{5}$?

2. How many eighths in $41\frac{5}{8}$?

3. What is $\frac{7}{12}$ of 504?

4. Write $\frac{9}{100}$ of a km in millimetres.

5. What fraction of 10 litres is 5240 ml?

6. What fraction of a leap year is one weekend?

7. How many sixths in $23\frac{5}{6}$?

8. How many ninths in $36\frac{1}{9}$?

9. What is $\frac{1}{13}$ of 156?

10. What fraction of £20 is £2.25?

11. What fraction of 1 m is 25 mm?

12. What fraction of a week is 56 hours?

13. How many tenths in $19\frac{9}{10}$?

14. How many sevenths in $14\frac{6}{7}$?

15. How many twelfths in $25\frac{7}{12}$?

16. What fraction of day is 24 minutes?

 **Training Tips**

 When dealing with large numbers and fractions use your × and ÷ knowledge.

 To find $\frac{4}{5}$ of a number you could find one fifth and then multiply the answer by 4.

Ratio and proportion

Alex has 1 marble for every 2 that Hattie has.
This means that if Alex has 4 marbles then Hattie has 8.

The ratio of black marbles to white marbles in this pattern is 1 to every 2. The proportion of black marbles to white marbles in the whole pattern is 1 in 3.

Bronze

What is the ratio and proportion of black and white marbles in these patterns?

1. ○○○●○○○●

2. ●●○○○○●●○○○

3. ●●●●○○
   ●●●●○○

4. ○○○○●●○○
   ○○●●○○○○

5. ○○○●●○○○●●

6. ○●●●○○○
   ○●●●○○○

7. ○○●●●●○○●●
   ●●○○●●●●○○

8. ●○○●○●○●●○

Can you make up some of your own?

Silver

Try these problems about ratio and proportion:

1. Pat needs 200 g of cranberries to make half a litre of cranberry sauce. How many grams of cranberries does she need to make 2 litres of cranberry sauce?

2. One stock cube makes 250 ml of gravy. How many stock cubes are needed to make 1 and a half litres of gravy?

3. 500 g of stuffing is needed to serve 8 people. How much is needed for 12 people?

4. 250 ml of water is needed for 2 potatoes. How much water is needed for 24 potatoes?

5. Carrots must be cooked in 300 ml of water per kilogram. How much water is needed for 3 kg of carrots?

6. If each person has two knives and three forks, how many pieces of cutlery must 8 people have?

7. Each person has on average 150 peas. How many people will 750 peas serve?

8. Roast turkey needs to be cooked for 50 minutes per kilogram. How long does a 7 kg turkey need to be cooked for?

Gold

Try these tricky problems:

1. Stevie shares out £35 with Bruce. He gives Bruce £2 for every £3 he takes for himself. How much does Bruce receive?

2. At the rock concert there are 2 boys for every 3 girls. There are 600 people at the concert. How many are girls?

3. Cola and water are the favourite drinks at the concert. If 4 colas are drunk for every 6 waters, how many colas are drunk if 500 drinks are sold in total?

4. T–shirts outsell posters by 4 to 1. If 36 posters are sold, how many T–shirts are sold?

5. If the concert has 5 rock songs to 2 love songs and there are 14 songs sung, how many are love songs?

6. After the concert Bruce signs autographs. He signs 3 postcards for every 5 CDs. If he signs 72 autographs, how many are on CDs?

7. In the car park there are 450 cars. For every 10 driven by boys there are 5 driven by girls. How many cars are driven by boys?

8. Bruce shares out the profits of the concert with Stevie. For every £5 he gives Stevie, he takes £12. If £204 was made in profit, how much does Stevie get?

Training Tips

'Two to every three' compares part to part. It is the same as 'two in every five'.

Ratios can be written with a colon instead of 'to every'. For example 1 to every 2 can be written as 1:2.

Fractions and decimals

Look at this decimal. See how much each digit is worth.

 2.75

2 wholes   7 tenths   5 hundredths

Bronze

a) What is each of the bold digits worth?

1. **5**.28

2. 9.**4**8

3. 6.6**6**

4. 11.4**5**

5. 12.7**8**

6. 13.**9**2

7. 10.0**1**

8. **9**.89

b) Put these decimals in order – smallest first:

1. 4.41   3.73   7.53   5.37   4.51

2. 8.89   8.98   9.88   8.88   9.99

3. 7.65   5.76   6.67   6.57   7.06

4. 14.14   41.41   14.41   44.11   44.44

5. 12.34   14.23   12.41   14.24   13.42

6. 18.93   19.38   19.89   18.91   19.88

7. 15.86   18.65   15.68   16.85   18.66

8. 13.74   14.37   13.41   14.77   17.14

Silver

a) What is each of the bold digits worth?

1. 7.**6**14

2. **5**.823

3. 9.95**2**

4. 1**2**.023

5. 7.**9**02

6. 8.97**3**

7. 11.79**3**

8. 10.03**5**

b) Put these decimals in order – smallest first:

1. 4.424   2.442   4.442   2.444

2. 7.878   7.778   8.787   7.887

3. 6.577   5.776   6.775   6.557

4. 2.119   1.922   2.112   2.992

5. 14.564   15.444   15.645   14.665

6. 11.034   10.444   11.403   11.434

7. 10.011   11.101   11.01   11.111

8. 9.257   7.532   9.527   9.725

Gold

a) What is each of the bold digits worth?

1. 7**2**.227

2. 89.9**9**8

3. 76.0**9**3

4. 25.6**3**3

5. 34.64**7**

6. 101.**8**92

7. 98.**0**24

8. 88.**8**03

b) Put these decimals in order – smallest first:

1. 33.351   35.533   31.355   33.551

2. 10.001   10.110   10.101   10.000

3. 45.545   54.544   44.504   55.445

4. 23.675   33.765   32.667   33.557

5. 67.706   67.667   67.767   76.667

6. 42.524   45.254   45.554   45.205

7. 101.011   111.101   111.110   110.001

8. 100.023   123.002   103.301   323.132

 Training Tips

 Numbers to the left of the decimal point are *whole* numbers.

 When ordering decimals, start reading their size from the left and work towards the right.

Fractions and decimals

Rounding to the nearest whole or tenth

Example	*Example*
6.7 rounded to the nearest whole number is 7	6.38 rounded to the nearest tenth is 6.40
22.2 rounded to the nearest whole number is 22	67.87 rounded to the nearest tenth is 67.90

Bronze

Silver

Gold

a) Round these to the nearest whole number:

1. 1.4

2. 23.6

3. 145.7

4. 131.8

5. 18.3

6. 49.7

7. 108.5

8. 19.5

a) Round these to the nearest whole number:

1. 20.7

2. 62.77

3. 247.39

4. 345.67

5. 23.81

6. 46.45

7. 101.91

8. 89.29

a) Round these decimals to the nearest tenth:

1. 2.785

2. 4.732

3. 8.276

4. 5.555

5. 89.351

6. 75.469

7. 39.442

8. 65.785

b) Round these lengths to the nearest metre:

1. 7.4 m

2. 3.2 m

3. 1.9 m

4. 4.5 m

5. 6.8 m

6. 1.4 m

7. 4.8 m

8. 8.3 m

b) Round these decimals to the nearest tenth:

1. 4.42

2. 8.12

3. 41.56

4. 56.75

5. 43.34

6. 73.28

7. 37.96

8. 87.05

b) Round these measures to the nearest tenth:

1. 1.567 ml

2. 6.754 km

3. 12.984 cm

4. 5.049 kg

5. 23.845 cm

6. 53.342 kg

7. 61.093 ml

8. 101.093 km

Training Tips

When rounding decimals, it helps to start reading the decimal from the right and work towards the left.

Understanding decimals will help you handle your money – and vice versa!

Recognising the equivalence between decimals and fractions

Decimals are another way of writing fractions.

> 0.05 is the same as $\frac{5}{100}$
>
> 8.35 is the same as $8\frac{35}{100}$
>
> 7.405 metres is the same as 7 metres, 40 centimetres and 5 millimetres
>
> 9.341 m is the same as 9 m, 34 cm and 1 mm

Bronze

a) Write these decimals as fractions:

1. 0.50
2. 0.75
3. 0.25
4. 0.10
5. 0.20
6. 0.35
7. 1.45
8. 1.89

b) Write these fractions as decimals:

1. $\frac{25}{100}$
2. $\frac{7}{100}$
3. $\frac{77}{100}$
4. 4 and $\frac{45}{100}$
5. 6 and $\frac{75}{100}$
6. $\frac{25}{50}$
7. $\frac{15}{20}$
8. 3 and $\frac{40}{50}$

Silver

a) What are the decimal fraction equivalents of the following measurements?

1. 2 m, 32 cm and 6 mm
2. 10 m, 67 cm and 7 mm
3. 8 m, 32 cm and 9 mm
4. 44 m, 44 cm and 4 mm
5. 3 m, 13 cm and 2 mm
6. 19 m, 15 cm and 4 mm
7. 10 m, 5 cm and 8 mm
8. 29 m, 36 cm and 9 mm

b) Write each of these decimals as a fraction:

1. 0.37
2. 4.1
3. 8.02
4. 0.04
5. 3.85
6. 7.56
7. 10.08
8. 12.67

Gold

You can use a calculator for these if you want to.

a) Which of these is less?

1. $\frac{7}{9}$ or $\frac{4}{5}$?
2. $\frac{3}{4}$ or $\frac{13}{17}$?
3. $\frac{23}{25}$ or $\frac{7}{8}$?
4. 0.25 or $\frac{6}{25}$?
5. 0.60 or $\frac{6}{7}$?
6. $\frac{24}{25}$ or $\frac{8}{9}$?
7. 0.625 or $\frac{4}{5}$?
8. $\frac{3}{7}$ or 0.45?

b) Place these in order – smallest first:

1. $\frac{14}{40}$, $\frac{6}{15}$, $\frac{23}{40}$, $\frac{8}{30}$
2. 0.45, $\frac{3}{5}$, 0.37, $\frac{4}{5}$
3. $\frac{12}{15}$, $\frac{5}{6}$, 0.70, 0.85
4. $\frac{13}{20}$, $\frac{17}{25}$, 0.69, 0.73
5. $\frac{8}{40}$, $\frac{9}{36}$, 0.35, 0.40
6. $\frac{14}{49}$, $\frac{15}{50}$, 0.28, 0.29
7. 0.68, 0.72, 0.69, $\frac{2}{3}$
8. $\frac{12}{48}$, $\frac{14}{52}$, $\frac{16}{56}$, 0.33

Training Tips

Learn the decimal equivalents of these fractions:

$\frac{1}{1000}$ = 0.001 $\frac{1}{8}$ = 0.125 $\frac{1}{3}$ = 0.3333333 $\frac{2}{3}$ = 0.6666666

Converting a fraction to a decimal using division

Fractions can be converted into decimals by dividing the numerator (top number) by the denominator (bottom number). You will need to use a calculator to do some of these.

Example

What is $\frac{1}{4}$ as a decimal fraction?

$1 \div 4 = 0.25$

If you are using your calculator you will need to round your answers to 2 or 3 decimal points.

Example

What is $\frac{1}{3}$ as a decimal fraction? Round your answer to 2 decimal places.

$\boxed{1} \div \boxed{3} = 0.333333333$

Round down to 0.33

Bronze

Convert these fractions to decimals. Round your answer to 2 decimal places.

1. $\frac{1}{2}$
2. $\frac{1}{4}$
3. $\frac{30}{100}$
4. $\frac{40}{100}$
5. $\frac{95}{100}$
6. $\frac{62}{100}$
7. $\frac{2}{4}$
8. $\frac{3}{4}$
9. $\frac{3}{3}$
10. $\frac{3}{5}$
11. $\frac{1}{5}$
12. $\frac{4}{10}$
13. $\frac{2}{5}$
14. $\frac{6}{10}$
15. $\frac{5}{5}$

Silver

Convert these fractions to decimals. Round your answer to 2 decimal places.

1. $\frac{5}{10}$
2. $\frac{3}{4}$
3. $\frac{2}{3}$
4. $\frac{4}{5}$
5. $\frac{1}{5}$
6. $\frac{1}{3}$
7. $\frac{2}{5}$
8. $\frac{4}{6}$
9. $\frac{6}{8}$
10. $\frac{5}{8}$
11. $\frac{3}{12}$
12. $\frac{5}{20}$
13. $\frac{10}{50}$
14. $\frac{18}{24}$
15. $\frac{32}{128}$

Gold

Convert these fractions to decimals. Round your answer to 2 decimal places.

1. $\frac{4}{5}$
2. $\frac{5}{15}$
3. $\frac{6}{48}$
4. $\frac{21}{28}$
5. $\frac{8}{40}$
6. $\frac{1}{3}$
7. $\frac{2}{3}$
8. $\frac{18}{20}$
9. $\frac{21}{25}$
10. $\frac{24}{27}$
11. $\frac{18}{36}$
12. $\frac{62}{63}$
13. $\frac{17}{27}$
14. $\frac{23}{24}$
15. $\frac{92}{99}$

Training Tips

 When rounding, remember '5 or more round up, less than 5 round down'.

 Try to estimate your answer before using your calculator.

Fractions, decimals and percentages

Use these facts to help you answer the questions.

Fractions, decimals and percentages facts

One whole = 100%   One half = 50%   One quarter = 25%   One tenth = 10%

$10\% = 0.1 = \frac{1}{10}$ $20\% = 0.2 = \frac{1}{5}$ $1\% = 0.01 = \frac{1}{100}$

$25\% = 0.25 = \frac{1}{4}$ $50\% = 0.5 = \frac{1}{2}$ $75\% = 0.75 = \frac{3}{4}$

$57\% = 0.57 = \frac{57}{100}$

Using a calculator

You can find difficult percentages by using a calculator. Look at this question.

526 football fans were asked who their favourite player was. 290 said David Beckham. What percentage said David Beckham was their favourite player?

Use a calculator.

Key in '290' then 'divide symbol' then '526' then '%'

You should have 55.133. Round this answer down to 55%.

Bronze

a) What percentage of these shapes is shaded?

1.

2.

3.

4.

5.

b) Try these questions without using a calculator:

1. What is 10% of 4 metres?

2. What is 75% of £100?

3. 25% of the people on the bus are wearing glasses. What percentage is not wearing glasses?

4. Dave got 30 out of 60 in his spelling test. Davina scored 35%. Who did better in the test – Dave or Davina?

5. 75% of Western Road Primary School's Year 6 class went on school journey. What percentage stayed behind?

c) Find these percentages by using halving and quartering.

1. 25% of £200

2. 50% of £260

3. 75% of £400

4. 75% of £300

5. 25% of £280

Training Tips

Remember as many percentage/fraction equivalents as you can:

$33\% = $ nearly $\frac{1}{3}$ $66\% = $ nearly $\frac{2}{3}$ $25\% = \frac{1}{4}$ $75\% = \frac{3}{4}$

Fractions, decimals and percentages

Silver

a) What percentages are equivalent to these decimals?

1. 0.41

2. 0.78

3. 0.24

4. 0.66

5. 0.12

b) Try these without using a calculator:

1. Find 60% of £60

2. Find 70% of 300kg

3. Find 25% of £300

4. Find 30% of £15

5. A pair of trainers cost £45. It has a 10% discount in a sale. What is the sale price of the trainers?

c) Find these percentages by halving and quartering:

1. 12.5% of £48 000

2. 6.25% of 12m

3. 25% of 16 000g

4. 5% of £14 000

5. 12.5% of 2400

Gold

Answer these questions using a calculator.
Round the answers up or down to the nearest percentage.

a) Here are the Maths Test scores for Year 6 Timber-Wolf Class at Western Road Primary. What are their percentages?

1. Ben – 139 out of 146

2. Tanya – 141 out of 146

3. Andrea – 125 out of 146

4. Richard – 132 out of 146

5. Priya – 140 out of 146

b) How many out of 146 did each of these children score?

1. Leo – 85%

2. Finley – 92%

3. Jamie – 89%

4. Bruce – 67%

5. Alexa – 99%

c) On the second test Year 6 had to answer 95 questions. What were their percentages?

1. Tanya – 88 out of 95

2. Richard – 92 out of 95

3. Leo – 81 out of 95

4. Bruce – 68 out of 95

5. Alexa – 94 out of 95

Training Tips

To find 1% of something, first find 10% then find 10% of THAT answer. You can work out any percentage by adding all the 10%, 5% and 1% answers together!

Understanding addition

Add, more, total, find the sum of, increase, how many altogether, all mean ADD!
Answer these quickly but carefully.

Bronze

a) Work these out:

1. Increase 170 by 47

2. Find the sum of 18, 67 and 125

3. Add 245 to 27

4. What is the total of 12, 54 and 88?

5. What is 45 more than 178?

6. Add 149, 20 and 85

7. Increase 34 by 49

8. What is the total of 119 and 91?

b) Fill in the blanks to complete these sums:

1. ☐ + 82 = 178

2. 634 + ☐ = 822

3. 559 + 142 = ☐

4. ☐ + 134 = 199

5. 36 + ☐ = 109

6. 478 + 354 = ☐

7. 156 + ☐ = 530

8. ☐ + 91 = 273

Silver

a) Work these out:

1. What is the total of 853 and 127?

2. Add 84, 26 and 59

3. Find the sum of 132, 243 and 576

4. Increase 798 by 106

5. Find the total of 675 and 391

6. Add 65, 21 and 128

7. What is the total of 541 and 283?

8. Increase 35 by 167

b) Total these shopping bills:

1. £34.28, £76.12 and £12.99

2. £15.98, £2.99 and £32.56

3. £48.17, £13.01 and £18.30

4. £90.65, £42.65 and £8.18

c) Fill in the blanks to complete these sums:

1. 387 + 3853 + ☐ = 6293

2. ☐ + 2978 + 826 = 5890

3. 1523 + ☐ + 465 = 3145

4. 553 + 679 + 1027 = ☐

Gold

a) Work these out:

1. What is the total of 6983, 3900 and 2285?

2. Increase 9032 by 4671

3. Add 8764, 63 and 3012

4. Find the sum of 1367, 4002 and 509

5. What is 9143, 6005 and 1812 altogether?

6. What is the total of 7901, 999 and 2762?

7. Find the sum of 832, 3981 and 5013

8. Increase 6393 by 7846

b) Use a written method to add these decimals:

1. 492.34 + 21.8 + 293.77

2. 978.87 + 579.04 + 42.1

3. 75.3 + 89.03 + 98.33

4. 586.12 + 73.69 + 34.07

5. 815.08 + 576.9 + 40.06

6. 24.51 + 975.41 + 123.8

7. 504.62 + 832.4 + 96.7

8. 187.03 + 163.19 + 142.74

Training Tips

 When you line up numbers to add them up, make sure the digits are in the correct columns!

 Remember the words for addition: add, more, total, sum of, increase.

Understanding subtraction

Take away, decrease, find the difference between, how much less, how many more make, all mean SUBTRACT.

Bronze

a) Work these out:

1. Take 70 from 361

2. How many less than 506 is 89?

3. Find the difference between 772 and 28

4. How much less is 143 than 983?

5. Subtract 45 from 657

6. Decrease 472 by 88

7. Take away 85 from 237

8. How many less than 105 is 45?

b) Fill in the blanks to complete these sums:

1. ☐ − 45 = 177

2. 423 − ☐ = 281

3. 632 − 67 = ☐

4. ☐ − 29 = 514

5. 798 − ☐ = 99

6. 196 − ☐ = 18

7. 369 − 83 = ☐

8. ☐ − 99 = 5

Silver

a) Work these out:

1. 4550 subtract 4005

2. What must I take from 9.4 to leave 3.8?

3. How much less is 239 than 1026?

4. What is the difference between 7.7 and 3.8?

5. Subtract 9241 from 9304.

6. Decrease 5631 by 3290.

7. Take away 4.6 from 10.3.

8. Subtract 3.5 from 10.3.

b) Fill in the blanks to complete these sums:

1. 4924 − ☐ = 261

2. 5.25 − 2.78 = ☐

3. 5789 − ☐ = 2396

4. 10.4 − 5.2 = ☐

5. 9.4 − ☐ = 4.9

6. 3493 − 1027 = ☐

7. 8731 − ☐ = 6642

8. 8.8 − 6.9 = ☐

Gold

a) Work these out:

1. 9482 − 5982 = ☐

2. 5820 − 1913 = ☐

3. 7345 − ☐ = 2592

4. 3009 − 2010 = ☐

5. ☐ − 2345 = 8294

6. ☐ − 1002 = 9341

7. 6603 − 4221 = ☐

8. 1005 − ☐ = 937

b) Subtract these decimals:

1. 572.3 − 276.45 = ☐

2. 227.9 − 114.88 = ☐

3. 737.8 − 612.52 = ☐

4. 935.92 − 789.44 = ☐

5. 340.12 − 128.77 = ☐

6. 722.6 − 601.78 = ☐

7. 554.91 − 345.67 = ☐

8. 101.01 − 99.09 = ☐

Training Tips

Try this game with a friend. Take it in turns to write down a three-digit number. The other person has five seconds to take it away from a thousand in their head or they lose a point. When you get really good, take the number away from 10,000!

Addition - adding most significant number

There are three main ways you learn to write down your 'working out' when you learn addition. We will look at each one in turn and give you plenty of practice.

Example

687 + 575 =

```
    687
 +  575
 ──────
   1100 ⎫
    150 ⎬  Add mentally from the top
     12 ⎭
 ──────
   1262
```

This has been calculated like this:

600 + 500 = 1100

80 + 70 = 150

7 + 5 = 12

Add them all together = 1262

Use this method to do these calculations. Set out your working clearly.

Bronze	**Silver**	**Gold**
1. 692 + 372	1. 7394 + 8243	1. 29922 + 4923
2. 731 + 529	2. 4923 + 3920	2. 67235 + 8923
3. 850 + 467	3. 6593 + 2994	3. 32104 + 7342
4. 231 + 944	4. 3029 + 5837	4. 98286 + 1585
5. 189 + 420	5. 5366 + 3218	5. 10344 + 9824
6. 555 + 347	6. 9228 + 1957	6. 48327 + 6333
7. 802 + 162	7. 8409 + 2113	7. 53817 + 3004
8. 239 + 682	8. 7883 + 1876	8. 85649 + 5667
9. 361 + 229	9. 1759 + 7930	9. 72655 + 8606
10. 403 + 509	10. 6507 + 2359	10. 18927 + 2934
11. 924 + 285	11. 5698 + 4019	11. 15871 + 65465
12. 109 + 827	12. 4568 + 3298	12. 21545 + 75891
13. 242 + 791	13. 1009 + 9001	13. 82674 + 45986
14. 187 + 808	14. 2794 + 5444	14. 33568 + 46355
15. 326 + 291	15. 1500 + 3449	15. 19991 + 91119
16. 483 + 525	16. 3053 + 2906	16. 50891 + 89463

Training Tips

When lining up calculations in columns, make sure units are under units, tens are under tens and so on.

Think clearly. Remember the value of the digits as you mentally calculate.

Addition – compensation

Example

842 + 386 =

```
    842
+   386
  ─────
   1242    (842 + 400)
−    14    (400 − 386)
  ─────
   1228
```

This method relies on good mental calculation skills and is very useful when you don't have a paper and pencil with you. Practise here with a paper and pencil. Set out your work clearly to show you understand how to do it.

Use the compensation method to answer these sums.

Bronze

1. 725 + 482
2. 992 + 283
3. 684 + 257
4. 825 + 126
5. 583 + 329
6. 391 + 782
7. 548 + 367
8. 195 + 206
9. 473 + 608
10. 227 + 910
11. 323 + 560
12. 236 + 788
13. 816 + 225
14. 972 + 103
15. 674 + 368
16. 156 + 459

Silver

1. 8363 + 2241
2. 9475 + 8824
3. 4598 + 6239
4. 3268 + 7069
5. 5613 + 2792
6. 1996 + 8012
7. 9007 + 1698
8. 2863 + 2668
9. 1269 + 6987
10. 3268 + 7669
11. 4139 + 5631
12. 8407 + 3269
13. 1001 + 9009
14. 4863 + 7006
15. 3874 + 1559
16. 5768 + 6992

Gold

1. 82031 + 2201
2. 49123 + 9980
3. 76912 + 6328
4. 29378 + 7226
5. 59821 + 5089
6. 33267 + 1395
7. 19856 + 8694
8. 63291 + 3787
9. 92213 + 4731
10. 45206 + 7238
11. 67911 + 57791
12. 24882 + 37913
13. 90167 + 43167
14. 86794 + 15578
15. 13795 + 70346
16. 79467 + 12475

Training Tips

Practise this method in your head when you're out shopping. Try adding up groceries at the checkout.

The more methods you can use, the easier the understanding becomes.

Addition - carrying

Example

1064 + 429 =

```
    T H T U
    1 0 6 4
+     4 2 9
  ─────────
    1 4 9 3
        1
```

The digits are lined in the correct columns.

- This sum has been solved by adding the units and carrying over any tens into the next column.
- Next the tens are added with any hundreds being carried into the hundreds column.
- When the hundreds are added and there is no thousands column to carry into, the answer is complete.

Use the carrying method to answer these sums.

 Bronze

1. 895 + 429
2. 364 + 358
3. 746 + 724
4. 237 + 196
5. 638 + 571
6. 322 + 337
7. 973 + 231
8. 764 + 193
9. 886 + 492
10. 988 + 837
11. 549 + 638
12. 357 + 706
13. 446 + 667
14. 387 + 222
15. 101 + 976
16. 394 + 409

 Silver

1. 8394 + 2238
2. 2512 + 6569
3. 4795 + 6779
4. 3789 + 5737
5. 1983 + 2020
6. 7106 + 9445
7. 3704 + 6912
8. 4653 + 4201
9. 1396 + 2837
10. 9767 + 6132
11. 7534 + 8219
12. 4293 + 7368
13. 1692 + 5371
14. 2267 + 1093
15. 3590 + 9938
16. 3769 + 8176

 Gold

1. 472848 + 78490
2. 889669 + 33687
3. 256452 + 88913
4. 734914 + 60197
5. 100267 + 49831
6. 591673 + 50009
7. 937194 + 25673
8. 349617 + 10269
9. 687246 + 97167
10. 167134 + 27297
11. 479761 + 593169
12. 619006 + 374568
13. 716767 + 160916
14. 379614 + 946103
15. 281634 + 866739
16. 928456 + 548724

 **Training Tips**

 When carrying, always start from the *right* and work towards the left.

 Look at your final answer – does it *look* correct?

Subtraction - counting up

Example

932 − 529 =

```
    932
 −  529
 ───────
     71   (added on 71 to make 600)
    300   (added on to 300 to make 900)
     32   (added on to 32 to make 932)
 ───────
    403   (the total of all the 'count ups' and
          the final answer to the calculation)
```

This is a good method to use mentally – learn to record it on paper as well.

Use the counting up method to answer these questions.
Remember to record your answers as neatly as you can.

 Bronze

1. 824 − 193
2. 792 − 488
3. 378 − 209
4. 597 − 328
5. 624 − 408
6. 973 − 785
7. 456 − 321
8. 298 − 89
9. 863 − 525
10. 176 − 99
11. 546 − 287
12. 923 − 777
13. 608 − 128
14. 366 − 219
15. 734 − 546
16. 467 − 329

 Silver

1. 7446 − 3684
2. 5833 − 2792
3. 2167 − 1039
4. 9834 − 6585
5. 3065 − 2231
6. 8319 − 4308
7. 6540 − 1367
8. 5465 − 2691
9. 6741 − 3521
10. 4137 − 2849
11. 1339 − 449
12. 8134 − 1247
13. 9257 − 7435
14. 3512 − 2941
15. 2291 − 1009
16. 6487 − 1649

Gold

1. 34672 − 12895
2. 83461 − 53598
3. 70079 − 31569
4. 13978 − 12036
5. 46752 − 22164
6. 61354 − 41357
7. 23347 − 11689
8. 42454 − 32135
9. 51945 − 37151
10. 61943 − 51814
11. 90214 − 43287
12. 71339 − 31350
13. 25613 − 14658
14. 80093 − 79471
15. 91344 − 82704
16. 36691 − 27319

 **Training Tips**

 Talk through each calculation in your mind – be aware of what you are doing as you do it!

 Check your answer by using the inverse method (adding the answer to the number you subtracted).

Subtraction - compensation

Example

394 − 189 =

```
   394
−  189
  ─────
   194   (394 − 200)
+   11   (because 200 − 189 = 11)
  ─────
   205
```

This method is useful for mental calculations. But you still need to practise recording it on paper.

**Answer these using the compensation method.
Remember to set out your work as neatly as you can.**

 Bronze

1. 724 − 278
2. 938 − 382
3. 497 − 157
4. 682 − 558
5. 364 − 235
6. 812 − 686
7. 329 − 251
8. 508 − 284
9. 653 − 417
10. 197 − 105
11. 763 − 447
12. 391 − 216
13. 546 − 378
14. 406 − 333
15. 964 − 826
16. 792 − 639

 Silver

1. 8395 − 5619
2. 7023 − 6721
3. 6719 − 1561
4. 9143 − 5646
5. 5565 − 3599
6. 3074 − 2813
7. 8792 − 6324
8. 1760 − 1389
9. 9638 − 8154
10. 2424 − 1036
11. 7861 − 6522
12. 6108 − 2650
13. 3216 − 2889
14. 4853 − 3195
15. 8132 − 6557
16. 5534 − 4068

 Gold

1. 45229 − 14988
2. 99003 − 31776
3. 64132 − 45779
4. 30994 − 26878
5. 79134 − 65273
6. 56795 − 42371
7. 20981 − 16398
8. 86340 − 54983
9. 16549 − 12856
10. 73154 − 62271
11. 56794 − 32109
12. 98347 − 77338
13. 29731 − 10679
14. 44692 − 38410
15. 56884 − 27415
16. 88903 − 31887

 **Training Tips**

 Always show your method – even if you get the answer wrong!

 Learning these informal methods will increase your mental maths skills.

Subtraction – decomposition

Here are two methods you may use:

1. Partitioning

$$854 \longrightarrow 800 + 50 + 4$$
$$-386 \longrightarrow \underline{300 + 80 + 6}$$
$$400 + 60 + 8$$

2. Standard method

$$854 \longrightarrow {}^7\cancel{8}\,{}^{14}\cancel{5}\,{}^1 4$$
$$-386 \longrightarrow \underline{3\ \ 8\ \ 6}$$
$$4\ \ 6\ \ 8$$

Bronze

Work these out:

1. 682 − 376
2. 947 − 289
3. 761 − 419
4. 308 − 127
5. 446 − 385
6. 837 − 559
7. 564 − 305
8. 197 − 108
9. 273 − 146
10. 806 − 741
11. 472 − 286
12. 710 − 537
13. 573 − 409
14. 635 − 428
15. 997 − 769
16. 567 − 431

Silver

Work these out:

1. 4967 − 3959
2. 9799 − 5828
3. 7915 − 1327
4. 9249 − 8481
5. 6378 − 4611
6. 3790 − 2118
7. 8097 − 6573
8. 2651 − 1094
9. 7561 − 3215
10. 1853 − 1691
11. 6818 − 4289
12. 4345 − 1029
13. 9776 − 8086
14. 5473 − 3249
15. 8651 − 6568
16. 7084 − 6108

Gold

a) Work these out:

1. 78429 − 42887
2. 80156 − 48891
3. 59131 − 33245
4. 93724 − 80695
5. 48719 − 32846
6. 25739 − 10846
7. 66088 − 45713
8. 74617 − 59815

b) Now try these. Find the difference between these numbers with different numbers of digits:

1. 48266 and 5788
2. 59731 and 816
3. 67188 and 8097
4. 69713 and 2154
5. 99133 and 9034
6. 1678 and 285
7. 68755 and 4376
8. 81035 and 7320

Training Tips

Practise subtracting decimals – make sure you line up the decimal points.

Ask a friend to give you a date in history – AD or BC. Work out how many years ago it was.

Multiplication - grid method

Example   82 x 38 =

Using a grid shows clearly which numbers are being multiplied.
Always approximate first so you will know if your answer is sensible.

82 × 38 is approximately 80 × 40 = 3200

×	30	8		
80	2400	640	=	3040
2	60	16	=	76
			=	3116

 Bronze

a) Use the grid method to solve these calculations. Remember to approximate first.

1. 572 × 7
2. 924 × 8
3. 278 × 4
4. 985 × 3
5. 882 × 6
6. 761 × 5
7. 601 × 9
8. 199 × 2

b) Now try these:

1. 38 × 49
2. 94 × 83
3. 66 × 44
4. 29 × 79
5. 58 × 37
6. 23 × 19
7. 45 × 39
8. 84 × 17

 Silver

a) Use the grid method to solve these calculations. Remember to approximate first.

1. 6835 × 3
2. 7461 × 2
3. 3205 × 5
4. 8367 × 4
5. 2019 × 8
6. 1917 × 7
7. 9831 × 6
8. 5641 × 9

b) Now try these:

1. 735 × 36
2. 601 × 48
3. 377 × 27
4. 193 × 13
5. 954 × 65
6. 826 × 49
7. 504 × 77
8. 438 × 68

 Gold

Use the grid method to solve these calculations. Remember to approximate first.

1. 8352 × 38
2. 4427 × 59
3. 6301 × 78
4. 5543 × 61
5. 9716 × 42
6. 7618 × 35
7. 8561 × 17
8. 2094 × 89
9. 1337 × 46
10. 6374 × 68
11. 4779 × 283
12. 8097 × 675
13. 3257 × 432
14. 9716 × 250
15. 1837 × 907
16. 2583 × 347

 **Training Tips**

 Using the grid method helps you understand the value of the digits and the numbers.

 Check your final answer against your approximation – if they are not close, check them both.

Multiplication - partitioning

This is the most common method of multiplying – you should be familiar with it already.

Short multiplication

246 × 9 =
Approximate first.
250 × 10 = 2500

```
    246
×     9
   2214
    45
```

Long multiplication

72 × 48 =
Approximate first.
70 × 50 = 3500

```
       72
×      48
     2880   (72 × 40)
      576   (72 × 8)
     3456   (add the two together)
       11
```

Check against the approximation.

Bronze

a) Try these short multiplications using partitioning. Remember to approximate first.

1. 923 × 4

2. 835 × 7

3. 156 × 3

4. 612 × 8

5. 929 × 9

6. 728 × 6

7. 527 × 2

8. 349 × 5

b) Try these long multiplications:

1. 72 × 43

2. 84 × 52

3. 63 × 27

4. 91 × 79

5. 36 × 18

6. 48 × 67

7. 32 × 27

8. 76 × 89

Silver

a) Try these ThHTU × U short multiplications:

1. 7384 × 3

2. 9334 × 7

3. 6317 × 6

4. 4431 × 8

5. 3068 × 9

6. 1274 × 5

7. 8063 × 2

8. 5612 × 1

b) Now try these HTU × TU long multiplications:

1. 429 × 62

2. 882 × 37

3. 239 × 48

4. 749 × 55

5. 906 × 71

6. 369 × 84

7. 527 × 93

8. 622 × 19

Gold

a) Try these HTU × HTU long multiplications:

1. 475 × 286

2. 692 × 585

3. 327 × 198

4. 914 × 467

5. 837 × 756

6. 627 × 384

7. 409 × 573

8. 286 × 197

b) Have a go at multiplying these decimals:

1. 7.45 × 38

2. 6.24 × 52

3. 3.18 × 65

4. 9.67 × 43

5. 8.84 × 72

6. 4.31 × 26

7. 5.03 × 97

8. 1.67 × 88

Training Tips

Remember to keep the place value when you multiply by tens, hundreds or thousands.

Approximate your answer first.

Division - using multiples of the divider

Look carefully at this division calculation.
It can be completed using knowledge of the multiples of the divider.

Method 1   268 ÷ 8

268 − 80 = 188 (10 × 8)

188 − 80 = 108 (10 × 8)

108 − 80 =   28 (10 × 8)

28 − 24   =   4 (3 × 8)

33 lots of 8 have been taken away so our answer is 33 remainder 4.

Method 2   974 ÷ 32

Approximate first. 1000 ÷ 30 = 33

974 − 320 = 654 (10 × 32)

654 − 320 = 334 (10 × 32)

334 − 320 =   14 (10 × 32)

Answer: $30\frac{14}{32}$

Bronze

Answer these using Method 1. Remember to approximate first and set your working out as clearly as you can.

1. 625 ÷ 6
2. 834 ÷ 9
3. 701 ÷ 5
4. 246 ÷ 4
5. 137 ÷ 7
6. 368 ÷ 2
7. 567 ÷ 3
8. 986 ÷ 8
9. 477 ÷ 7
10. 385 ÷ 5
11. 757 ÷ 6
12. 283 ÷ 9
13. 653 ÷ 4
14. 912 ÷ 2
15. 408 ÷ 7
16. 537 ÷ 8

Silver

Use Method 1 or 2 to answer these:

1. 738 ÷ 24
2. 695 ÷ 27
3. 374 ÷ 19
4. 981 ÷ 67
5. 583 ÷ 43
6. 461 ÷ 55
7. 264 ÷ 39
8. 197 ÷ 34
9. 806 ÷ 63
10. 537 ÷ 21
11. 672 ÷ 33
12. 914 ÷ 53
13. 822 ÷ 49
14. 365 ÷ 77
15. 489 ÷ 91
16. 671 ÷ 85

Gold

Use Method 1 or 2 to answer these:

1. 4825 ÷ 28
2. 7724 ÷ 62
3. 6018 ÷ 37
4. 1734 ÷ 44
5. 2956 ÷ 37
6. 3271 ÷ 53
7. 9816 ÷ 91
8. 5387 ÷ 72
9. 6731 ÷ 19
10. 2371 ÷ 82
11. 4437 ÷ 30
12. 7143 ÷ 53
13. 2462 ÷ 67
14. 5469 ÷ 45
15. 649 ÷ 88
16. 3827 ÷ 51

Training Tips

 Knowing your multiplication facts up to 10 x 10 and being able to multiply by 10 and 100 is a big help!

 Be clear in your writing – it can show how you're thinking.

Division – short and long division

Short division is dividing by a single digit number.

Example   194 ÷ 6

Approximate first. 200 ÷ 5 = 40

```
      34 r 2
 6) 194
   −180
     14
    −12
      2
```

Answer 34 r 2

Long division is dividing by a number with more than one digit.

Example

964 ÷ 38
Approximate first.

1000 ÷ 40 = 25

```
          25 r 14
    38) 964
       −760
        204
       −190
         14
```

Answer 25 r 14

Bronze

Answer these short division calculations. Give remainders where appropriate.

1. 762 ÷ 3
2. 589 ÷ 6
3. 938 ÷ 5
4. 671 ÷ 8
5. 208 ÷ 2
6. 367 ÷ 7
7. 481 ÷ 9
8. 846 ÷ 4
9. 773 ÷ 6
10. 137 ÷ 9
11. 628 ÷ 2
12. 729 ÷ 5
13. 222 ÷ 8
14. 676 ÷ 4
15. 432 ÷ 7
16. 536 ÷ 6

Silver

Work out these long division sums:

1. 582 ÷ 25
2. 896 ÷ 62
3. 723 ÷ 34
4. 907 ÷ 71
5. 648 ÷ 24
6. 840 ÷ 35
7. 367 ÷ 41
8. 284 ÷ 19
9. 961 ÷ 93
10. 633 ÷ 72
11. 182 ÷ 39
12. 785 ÷ 21
13. 238 ÷ 48
14. 841 ÷ 67
15. 505 ÷ 55
16. 936 ÷ 73

Gold

Work out these long division sums:

1. 5872 ÷ 34
2. 4723 ÷ 56
3. 6791 ÷ 99
4. 7824 ÷ 22
5. 3015 ÷ 67
6. 2491 ÷ 82
7. 8632 ÷ 74
8. 1157 ÷ 13
9. 9257 ÷ 31
10. 4238 ÷ 64
11. 3269 ÷ 70
12. 6089 ÷ 35
13. 7335 ÷ 53
14. 8605 ÷ 28
15. 5938 ÷ 46
16. 2594 ÷ 86

Training Tips

You can divide decimal numbers by whole numbers using these methods.

You can check the answer of any division calculation by using the inverse.

Understanding multiplication

Look at this question: 4 + 7 × 5 = 39

Is the answer correct? The answer would be 55 if we add 4 and 7 and then multiply the answer by 5.

We can use brackets...

Now look at the calculation again.

4 + (7 × 5) = 39

4 + 35 = 39

Times, **multiplied by, product, multiple** and the '×' sign are all terms to do with multiplication. The inverse, or opposite, of multiplication is division.

Bronze

a) **Write out these calculations, putting in the brackets so they make sense:**

1. 6 + 8 × 9 = 78

2. 7 − 3 × 4 = 16

3. 2 × 6 + 7 = 19

4. 8 × 3 + 7 = 80

5. 9 − 7 × 3 = 6

6. 8 × 6 − 5 = 43

7. 1 + 9 × 2 = 19

8. 3 × 8 − 7 = 3

b) **Now try these:**

1. What is the product of 25 and 6?

2. What is double 43?

3. Multiply 21 by 7.

4. What is five times 18?

5. What is the multiple of 9 and 12?

6. What is 23 multiplied by 8?

7. What is the product of 13 and 7?

8. Multiply 35 and 6.

Silver

a) **Work these out:**

1. What is double 85?

2. Multiply 35 by 8

3. What is the product of 150 and 8?

4. Times 35 by 24.

5. Multiply 191 and 7.

6. What is the multiple of 82 and 13?

7. What is six times 23?

8. What is the product of 72 and 19?

b) **Use pencil and paper jottings and/or mental strategies to answer these:**

1. 0.4 × 7 = ☐

2. 25 × ☐ = 8000

3. 123 × 45 = ☐

4. ☐ × 67 = 1541

5. 1.25 × 8 = ☐

6. 72 × 5 = ☐

7. 32 × ☐ = 608

8. 2.4 × 8 = ☐

Gold

Work these out:

1. 245 × (56 − 38) = ☐

2. 357 × (71 − 59) = ☐

3. (22 + 69) × 745 = ☐

4. (18 − 7) × 632 = ☐

5. 601 × (98 − 77) = ☐

6. 485 × (41 − 25) = ☐

7. (66 + 27) × 113 = ☐

8. (63 + 22) × 705 = ☐

9. 537 × (46 − 18) = ☐

10. 124 × (92 − 29) = ☐

11. (54 + 12) × 305 = ☐

12. (71 − 67) × 918 = ☐

13. 276 × (25 + 4) = ☐

14. 428 × (39 + 17) = ☐

15. (99 − 37) × 143 = ☐

16. (61 − 16) × 232 = ☐

Training Tips

Use your multiplication skills to check the results of division calculations.

It doesn't matter which way round you multiply numbers – the answer is the same.

Understanding division

Share, divide, divided by, factor, remainder, divided into, quotient and the '/' and '÷' signs are all terms related to division.

Division is related to fractions.

$\frac{1}{4}$ of 24 is the same as $24 \div 4$

5 divided by 7 is the same as $\frac{5}{7}$

17 divided by 9 is the same as 1 and $\frac{8}{9}$

Bronze

Work these out:

1. Share 56 by 7

2. Divide 36 by 12

3. What is the remainder when 84 is divided by 7?

4. What are the factors of 24?

5. How many groups of 9 can be made from 83?

6. Divide 121 by 11.

7. Share 108 by 12.

8. What is the remainder when 96 is divided by 7?

Now have a go at these:

1. $168 \div 4 = \square$

2. $\square \div 31 = 70$

3. $\square \div 21 = 22$

4. $217 \div \square = 31$

5. $256 \div 8 = \square$

6. $301 \div 7 = \square$

7. $\square \div 15 = 23$

8. $\square \div 36 = 19$

Silver

Work these out:

1. Share 121 by 11

2. Divide 15 into 255

3. What are the factors of 84?

4. What is the remainder when you divide 853 by 29?

5. Divide 632 by 19.

6. Share 455 by 35.

7. What are the factors of 121?

8. Divide 703 by 101. What is the remainder?

Complete these:

1. $\frac{1}{5}$ of 30 is the same as $\square$ or $\square$

2. 6 divided by 7 is the same as $\square$

3. 21 divided by 13 is the same as $\square$

4. $\frac{1}{4}$ of 84 is the same as $\square$

5. 2.8 divided by 0.7 is the same as $\square$

6. 38 divided by 11 is the same as $\square$

7. $\frac{1}{3}$ of 270 is the same as $\square$

8. 9.6 divided by 3.2 is the same as $\square$

Gold

Work these out:

1. $6738 \div 265$

2. $(476 + 382) \div (566 - 352)$

3. 5602 divided by 245.

4. $2984 \div 35$

5. $(222 + 429) \div 81$

6. $1569 \div (234 - 108)$

7. $3691 \div 580$

8. 7296 divided by 193

9. $(896 - 279) \div 42$

10. $9989 \div 118$

11. $(923 - 101) \div (1502 - 1487)$

12. 4502 divided by 793

13. $6348 \div 456$

14. $(250 \div 10) + (529 \div 23)$

15. $(1793 + 3669) \div 102$

16. 9343 divided by 572

Training Tips

 A number cannot be divided by zero.

 Division is not 'commutative'. This means that $21 \div 7$ is not the same as $7 \div 21$.

Multiplication and division facts

Learning your times tables in really important.

Use your times tables knowledge to solve these multiplication and division questions.

Bronze

a) Work out:

1. $5 \times 6 =$
2. $4 \times 6 =$
3. $7 \times 5 =$
4. $9 \times 3 =$
5. $8 \times 6 =$
6. $3 \times 7 =$
7. $2 \times 8 =$
8. $8 \times 7 =$
9. $10 \times 6 =$
10. $8 \times 9 =$

b) Now try these:

1. $56 \div 7 =$
2. $24 \div 3 =$
3. $63 \div 9 =$
4. $49 \div 7 =$
5. $56 \div 8 =$
6. $48 \div 6 =$
7. $45 \div 5 =$
8. $72 \div 8 =$
9. $36 \div 6 =$
10. $32 \div 4 =$

Silver

a) Work out:

1. $1.2 \times 4 =$
2. $8 \times 0.3 =$
3. $0.4 \times 7 =$
4. $0.8 \times 4 =$
5. $6 \times 0.7 =$
6. $0.9 \times 6 =$
7. $0.6 \times 6 =$
8. $12 \times 7 =$
9. $9 \times 9 =$
10. 8×12.5

b) Now try these:

1. $3.5 \div 7 =$
2. $1.8 \div 2 =$
3. $54 \div 0.9 =$
4. $60 \div 1.2 =$
5. $16 \div 0.4 =$
6. $4.5 \div 9 =$
7. $7.2 \div 8 =$
8. $28 \div 0.4 =$
9. $4.8 \div 6 =$
10. $84 \div 1.2 =$

Gold

a) Work out:

1. $50 \times 3 =$
2. $8 \times 70 =$
3. $12 \times 11 =$
4. $40 \times 9 =$
5. $90 \times 7 =$
6. $1.2 \times 6 =$
7. $0.7 \times 9 =$
8. $80 \times 6 =$
9. $0.2 \times 12 =$
10. $12 \times 12 =$

b) Now try these:

1. $250 \div 5 =$
2. $360 \div 40 =$
3. $720 \div 8 =$
4. $49 \div 0.7 =$
5. $3.2 \div 0.4 =$
6. $4.8 \div 6 =$
7. $121 \div 11 =$
8. $9.6 \div 12 =$
9. $6.4 \div 0.8 =$
10. $700 \div 100 =$

Training Tips

Practise your tables once a week.

Remember that multiplication and division are opposites. Learn your multiplication tables and division will follow!

Mental strategies

1. Using factors

Example

Look at the sum and find factors

36 x 24 = 36 x (6 x 4)

= (36 x 6) x 4

= 216 x 4

= 864

2. Multiplying by 49 or 51

Example

To multiply by 49 or 51 we multiply by 50 and then adjust.

49 x 16 = (16 x 50) – (16 x 1)

= 800 – 16

= 784

Bronze

a) Use factors to solve:

1. $21 \times 5 =$
2. $24 \times 8 =$
3. $35 \times 7 =$
4. $42 \times 3 =$
5. $27 \times 6 =$
6. $112 \div 14 =$
7. $96 \div 6 =$
8. $224 \div 16 =$
9. $306 \div 9 =$
10. $255 \div 15 =$

b) Work out:

1. $21 \times 16 =$
2. $51 \times 14 =$
3. $49 \times 15 =$
4. $19 \times 19 =$
5. $49 \times 12 =$
6. $39 \times 13 =$
7. $99 \times 23 =$
8. $79 \times 21 =$
9. $89 \times 49 =$
10. $71 \times 18 =$

Silver

a) Use factors to solve:

1. $48 \times 7 =$
2. $32 \times 3 =$
3. $28 \times 4 =$
4. $45 \times 8 =$
5. $56 \times 7 =$
6. $480 \div 12 =$
7. $288 \div 16 =$
8. $432 \div 24 =$
9. $288 \div 16 =$
10. $576 \div 32 =$

b) Work out:

1. $71 \times 22 =$
2. $61 \times 31 =$
3. $59 \times 42 =$
4. $49 \times 18 =$
5. $99 \times 14 =$
6. $29 \times 23 =$
7. $79 \times 34 =$
8. $61 \times 21 =$
9. $31 \times 44 =$
10. $69 \times 71 =$

Gold

a) Use factors to solve:

1. $112 \times 7 =$
2. $96 \times 2 =$
3. $121 \times 6 =$
4. $108 \times 9 =$
5. $320 \times 3 =$
6. $504 \div 42 =$
7. $624 \div 24 =$
8. $192 \div 32 =$
9. $448 \div 56 =$
10. $441 \div 63 =$

b) Work out:

1. $101 \times 13 =$
2. $91 \times 26 =$
3. $111 \times 34 =$
4. $149 \times 17 =$
5. $99 \times 26 =$
6. $89 \times 41 =$
7. $199 \times 51 =$
8. $91 \times 84 =$
9. $121 \times 31 =$
10. $101 \times 91 =$

 **Training Tips**

 Think back to your times tables to find the factors that are easier to multiply.

 Estimate your answers before multiplying by 51 or 49.

Mental strategies

1. Partitioning

You can use partitioning for multiplication.

Example

$24 \times 7 = (20 \times 7) + (4 \times 7)$

$\quad\quad\quad = 140 + 28$

$\quad\quad\quad = 168$

2. Adding

You can create a new times table by adding together two tables you already know!

Example

$18 \times 16 = (10 \times 16) + (8 \times 16)$

$\quad\quad\quad\quad = 160 + 128$

$\quad\quad\quad\quad = 288$

Bronze

a) Use partitioning to solve:

1. $19 \times 8 =$
2. $25 \times 6 =$
3. $18 \times 9 =$
4. $22 \times 3 =$
5. $27 \times 7 =$
6. $24 \times 5 =$
7. $21 \times 7 =$
8. $16 \times 12 =$
9. $23 \times 11 =$
10. $17 \times 13 =$

b) Use adding to create the 19 times table:

× 9	× 10	× 19
9	10	19
18	20	38

Silver

a) Work out:

1. $45 \times 3 =$
2. $29 \times 9 =$
3. $56 \times 7 =$
4. $67 \times 4 =$
5. $92 \times 6 =$
6. $84 \times 12 =$
7. $73 \times 9 =$
8. $113 \times 8 =$
9. $6.3 \times 7 =$
10. $8.9 \times 9 =$

b) Use adding to create the 23 times table:

× 20	× 3	× 23
20	3	23
40	6	46

Gold

a) Work out:

1. $4.7 \times 2 =$
2. $3.8 \times 3 =$
3. $7.2 \times 8 =$
4. $5.3 \times 9 =$
5. $2.9 \times 7 =$
6. $67 \times 11 =$
7. $48 \times 6 =$
8. $124 \times 5 =$
9. $108 \times 9 =$
10. $135 \times 7 =$

b) Use adding to create the 57 times table:

× 50	× 7	× 57
50	7	57
100	14	114
150	21	171

 **Training Tips**

 Remember when you multiply by 10 (or 20 or 30...) each digit moves one place to the left.

 Try to make new times tables by adding. Learn these too!

Using a calculator

If a question has brackets in it you must **work out the brackets first** using your calculator. Write this answer down and then finish working out the sum.

6.45 kg − 3.25 kg =

We type 6.45 − 3.25 = 3.2

The answer is 3.2 kg

What is £10.99 less 25%?

We type 10.99 − 25 % = 8.2425

Round up the answer is £8.24

Bronze

a) Use your calculator to solve these two step problems:

1. 4 × (34 − 13) =

2. (190 − 84) × 2 =

3. 500 − (23 × 8) =

4. 325 − (12 × 12) =

5. (130 × 11) − 1200 =

6. (4 × 6) + (9 × 19) =

7. (26 × 3) − (5 × 11) =

8. (41 × 7) + (0.2 × 71) =

b) Solve these measures problems using your calculator:

1. £4.56 − £1.27 =

2. 235 m × 4 =

3. 1.67 l − 0.58 l =

4. 3.34 kg × 8 =

5. £127.34 − £108.39 =

6. 1250 m − 792 m =

7. 839 kg − 142 kg =

8. £18.23 × 6 =

Silver

a) Use your calculator to solve these multi–step problems:

1. (32 + 24) × (18 − 4) =

2. (123 − 116) × (908 − 889) =

3. (23 × 5) − 720 =

4. (56 − 2) × (34 + 1) −6 =

b) Solve these measures problems using your calculator:

1. £2.56 − ☐ = £1.29

2. 23.56 kg ÷ 4 =

3. 679 ml + 435 ml =

4. 3.75 km × 45 =

5. £123.95 + £508.95 =

c) Solve these percentage problems using your calculator:

1. £3.56 less 25%

2. £12.99 plus 15%

3. £18.99 less 20%

4. £109.89 plus 40%

Gold

a) Use your calculator to solve these multi–step problems:

1. (92 + 54) ÷ (193 −187) =

2. (467 − 328) × (105 − 79) =

3. (86 × 13) − 1068 =

4. (24 + 47) × (108 − 69) − 6 =

b) Solve these measures problems using your calculator:

1. £862.94 − ☐ = £352.78

2. 194.5 kg ÷ 7 =

3. 1.893 l + 435 ml =

4. 3056 m × 83 =

5. £1008.32 + £673.58 =

c) Solve these percentage problems using your calculator:

1. £9.34 less 23%

2. £9.99 plus 17%

3. £168.97 less 29%

4. £1555.89 plus 49%

Training Tips

Remember that calculators don't put in all the decimals, so £3.20 will look like 3.2.

Remember to use your brain before your calculator!

Checking results of calculations

It is important that we check our answers to make sure they make sense and that we have not made a mistake. Over the next two pages you will practise this skill.

The inverse operation using a calculator

When you are using a calculator to work out sums, check you have got the right answer by putting in the inverse operation.

> If you have worked out $345 \times 32 = 11040$
>
> check this is correct by typing in
>
> $11040 \div 32 = 345$
>
> You were correct.

Divisibility tests

You can check whether your division sums are correct by using these 'divisibility tests'.

By 3

A number is divisible by 3 if when you add up the digits in the number the answer divides by 3 with no remainders.

> *Example*
>
> $345621 = 3 + 4 + 5 + 6 + 2 + 1 = 21$
>
> Yes 21 divides perfectly by 3, seven times, so 345621 must be divisible by three.

By 2, 4 and 8

A number is divisible by 2 if the last digit is divisible by 2.

A number is divisible by 4 if the last two digits are divisible by 4.

A number is divisible by 8 if the last three digits are divisible by 8.

> *Example*
>
> 234532 – is divisible by 2 ($\frac{2}{2}$) and 4 ($\frac{32}{4}$) but not 8 ($\frac{532}{8}$)

By 5 and 10

If a number ends in 5 or 0 then it is divisible by 5.

If a number ends in a 0 then it is divisible by 10

By 6 and 9

If a number is divisible by 2 AND 3 then it is divisible by 6.

> *Example*
>
> 928566 is divisible by 2 (464283) and 3 (309522) so it must be divisible by 6.
>
> If the sum of the digits is divisible exactly by 9 then the number is divisible by 9.
>
> $6489 = 6 + 4 + 8 + 9 = 27$ ... which is divisible by 9!

Checking results of calculations

Check the following sums using your calculator. Mark them right or wrong.

Bronze

1. 289 × 13 = 3767
2. 43 488 ÷ 3624 = 12
3. 671 − 41 = 626
4. 164 × 127 = 21 828
5. 7176 ÷ 79 = 92

Silver

1. 1789 × 16 = 28 624
2. 2584 ÷ 152 = 18
3. 7293 − 512 = 6783
4. 137 × 98 = 13 426
5. 7245 ÷ 70 = 105

Gold

1. 92 × 45 = 4410
2. 11 772 ÷ 108 = 109
3. 3268 − 1783 = 1458
4. 176 × 143 = 25 168
5. 6745 ÷ 71 = 95

Check whether these sums are divisible exactly. Then complete the sums.

1. 918 ÷ 9 =
2. 3265 ÷ 10 =
3. 34 568 ÷ 4 =
4. 42 171 ÷ 3 =
5. 127 979 ÷ 5 =
6. 9208 ÷ 2 =
7. 1217 ÷ 4 =
8. 966 ÷ 6 =
9. 12 664 ÷ 8 =
10. 255 550 ÷ 10 =

1. 632 701 ÷ 9 =
2. 19 224 ÷ 8 =
3. 98 016 ÷ 4 =
4. 62 001 ÷ 3 =
5. 1 290 554 ÷ 5 =
6. 1048 ÷ 2 =
7. 71 507 ÷ 4 =
8. 468 ÷ 6 =
9. 10 783 ÷ 8 =
10. 196 325 ÷ 10 =

1. 1 634 301 ÷ 9 =
2. 18 327 ÷ 8 =
3. 108 443 ÷ 4 =
4. 73 023 ÷ 3 =
5. 22 345 ÷ 5 =
6. 2227 ÷ 2 =
7. 109 752 ÷ 4 =
8. 978 ÷ 6 =
9. 93 136 ÷ 8 =
10. 2 876 320 ÷ 10 =

Training Tips

Checking every sum will make sure you won't make mistakes.

Checking sums:
Change the order to check.
Do an equivalent sum.

Length, mass and capacity - understanding names

Knowing the names of all the metric and imperial units of measurement is very useful.
You also need to know how they relate to one another, for example '1 mile is about 1600 metres'.

Test or improve your knowledge by answering these.
Use the table on page 43 to help you answer these questions.

Bronze

a) Write the full word or words for these abbreviations:

1. km   2. m

3. cm   4. mm

5. kg   6. g

7. l   8. cl

b) What are the following measurements? (Use the correct units.)

1. Half a kilometre

2. A quarter of a metre

3. A tenth of a litre

4. Three-quarters of a kilometre

c) Now try these:

1. What is 1.8 m in centimetres?

2. What is 6.2 kg in grams?

3. What is 427 cm in metres?

4. What is 3500 ml in litres?

Silver

a) Have a go at these:

1. 1 tonne equals how many kilograms?

2. 1 litre equals how many millilitres?

3. 1 centilitre equals how many millilitres?

4. How many ounces are there in one pound?

b) Convert these larger metric units to smaller ones:

1. Write 5.250 km in metres

2. Write 3.25 litres in millilitres

3. Write 4.67 kg in grams

4. Write 345 metres in centimetres

c) Approximate equivalents means 'roughly the same'. Have a go at completing these:

1. 8 kilometres is approximately equivalent to how many miles?

2. 30 g is approximately equivalent to how many ounces?

3. 1 kg is approximately equivalent to how many pounds?

4. 4.5 litres is approximately equivalent to how many gallons?

Gold

a) Convert these smaller units to larger ones:

1. Write 650 grams in kilograms

2. Write 5 centimetres in metres

3. Write 34 millilitres in litres

4. Write 345 metres in km

5. Write 873 grams in kilograms

6. Write 609 millilitres in l

7. Write 1200 centimetres in metres

8. Write 3405 millilitres in litres

b) Work these out:

1. What is a thousandth of 3 km?

2. What is a thousandth of 40 kg?

3. What is one hundredth of 24 metres?

4. What is one tenth of 5 litres?

5. What is one thousandth of 5.6 kg?

6. What is one tenth of 3.67 metres?

7. What is one hundredth of 245 litres?

8. What is one thousandth of 4.05 kg?

Training Tips

Your knowledge of decimals will help when you work with metric units.

Learn the facts and how to translate each metric unit into an imperial one and vice versa.

Length, mass and capacity – using suitable units

Using the right unit of measure is important. Imagine using a ruler that was 30m long!

Metric and Imperial conversions (approximate)

1 litre = 1.8pts	1 gallon = 4.54 litres	
1 kilogram = 2.2lbs (pounds)	1 pound = 0.454g	1g = 0.035 oz
1 mile = 1.6km	5 miles = 8km	
1 foot = 30cm	1 metres = 3 feet, 3 inches	1 inch = 2.5cm

Bronze

a) Do you think that:

1. The classroom door is 2m, 6m or 8m high?

2. An apple weighs 500g, 1.5kg or 125g?

3. A can of pop has about 800ml, 3.5l or 350ml?

4. Your playground is about is 100km, 100m or 100cm long?

5. Your teacher is about 17.5m, 1.75m or 175m tall?

6. A pencil weighs 50kg, 50g or 500g?

b) Which unit of measurement would you use to measure the following?

1. The weight of a CD

2. The weight of TV set

3. The length of a grain of rice

4. The amount of water in the bath

5. The distance between London and Edinburgh

6. The amount of water in a tablespoon

Silver

a) Look at the imperial measures above. Select a sensible imperial and metric measure for each of the following:

1. Distance from Paris to London.

2. Amount of water in a swimming pool.

3. Weight of a yoghurt pot.

4. Length of this book.

b) Explain how you could measure:

1. The length of a roll of kitchen paper.

2. The weight of one pea.

3. The amount of water in a snowflake.

4. The length of the pages in this book laid end to end.

c) Think about these sports. Which units of measure might your see used?

1. The javelin

2. 100m sprint

3. Weight–lifting

4. High–jump

Gold

a) Estimate:

A dictionary:

1. Height   2. Weight

3. Length   4. Width

A double-decker bus:

1. Height   2. Weight

3. Length   4. Width

b) Use the information at the top of the page to answer these questions:

1. Is a centimetre larger or smaller than an inch?

2. Are there more or less than 40 inches in a metre?

3. Which is bigger 10,000 grams or 30 lbs?

4. I walked 12km at the weekend, how far is this in miles?

5. 1m + 2 inches is the same as 3 feet and ? cm?

c) Investigate 5 different measures you would find in a supermarket.

Training Tips

 Remember that time is a measure too.

 Kilo means a thousand.

Length, mass and capacity - reading scales 1

Once you have chosen which measuring instrument to use to measure
something, it's important that you can read it accurately!

Bronze

a) Look carefully at these different rulers.
What is the difference between the arrows in
centimetres?

1.

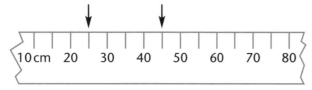

2.

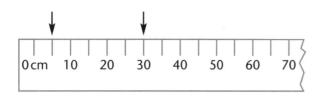

3.

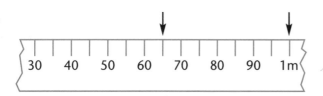

4.

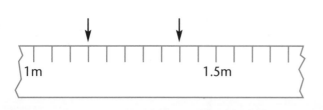

b) Add 80 ml to each cylinder. What is the new
water level?

1.    **2.**

3.    **4.**

c) Take 400 grams from each set of scales.
How much is left?

1. 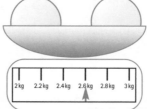   **2.**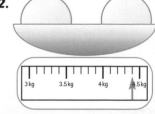

Length, mass and capacity – reading scales 1

 Silver

 Gold

a) Look at these rulers. What distance is the arrow pointing to in centimetres?

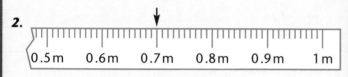

1.

0m   0.1m   0.2m   0.3m   0.4m   0.5m

2.

0.5m   0.6m   0.7m   0.8m   0.9m   1m

3.

1m   1.1m   1.2m   1.3m   1.4m   1.5m

4.

0m   0.1m   0.2m   0.3m   0.4m

b) How many grams are on each of these scales?

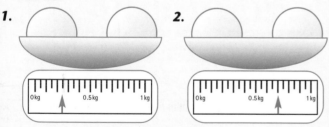

1.

0kg   0.5kg   1kg

2.

0kg   0.5kg   1kg

c) How many millilitres of water are in each of these cylinders?

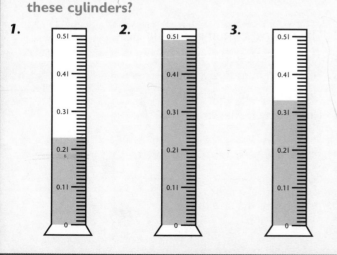

1.   **2.**   **3.**

a) What are these scales showing? Write your answer in the most sensible unit.

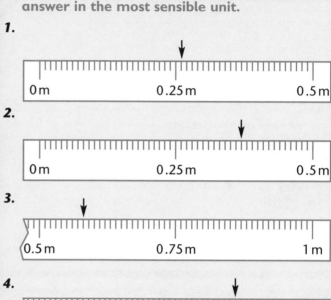

1.

0m   0.25m   0.5m

2.

0m   0.25m   0.5m

3.

0.5m   0.75m   1m

4.

0.5m   0.75m   1m

5.   **6.**

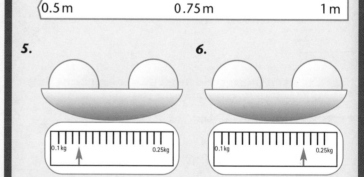

0.1kg   0.25kg

0.1kg   0.25kg

b) What do you think each of these instruments measures?

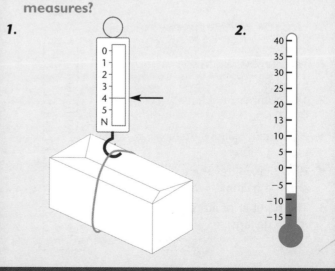

1.   **2.**

Length, mass and capacity - reading scales 2

Remember the key facts about measuring:

10 mm = 1 cm	1000 g = 1 kg	1000 ml = 1 l
100 cm = 1 m		
1000 m = 1 km		

Bronze

a) Convert these measures into kilograms, litres, metres or kilometres:

1. 1500 g   **2.** 250 ml   **3.** 600 cm

4. 3250 g   **5.** 500 ml   **6.** 750 m

7. 2100 g   **8.** 1500 ml   **9.** 150 cm

10. 8250 g

b) Round these measurements to the nearest whole unit:

1. 50.3 m   **2.** 4.7 l   **3.** 1.95 m

4. 1.85 kg   **5.** 4.202 kg **6.** 1.267 l

c) Round these measurements to the nearest kilogram, litre or metre;

1. 3576 ml   **2.** 721 cm   **3.** 1019 g

4. 8753 ml   **5.** 10567 cm

Silver

a) Convert these measures into kilograms, litres, metres or kilometres:

1. 2230 g   **2.** 110 ml   **3.** 730 cm

4. 1950 g   **5.** 320 ml   **6.** 1390 m

7. 7350 g   **8.** 3280 ml   **9.** 760 cm

10. 8110 g

c) Use this centimetres and inches ruler to approximate the following:

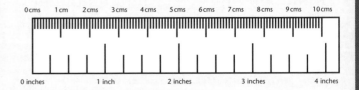

1. The number of mm in $\frac{1}{2}$ an inch.

2. The number of inches in 7.5 cm.

3. How many cm in 2 inches?

4. How many cm in 3 inches?

5. How many inches in 90 mm?

b) Use the scale opposite to approximate the following:

1. The number of litres in 3.5 gallons.

2. The number of gallons in 5 litres.

3. How many gallons there are in 12 litres.

4. How many litres there are in 4 gallons.

5. The number of litres in 2.5 gallons.

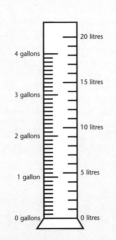

Length, mass and capacity – reading scales 2

Gold

a) Convert these measures into kilograms, litres, metres or kilometres:

1. 1062 g 2. 428 ml 3. 139 cm
4. 364 g 5. 18 ml 6. 7116 m
7. 9067 g 8. 1873 ml 9. 24 cm
10. 1679 g

b) Use the scale opposite to approximate the following:

1. 0.5 gallons in ml
2. 4 l in gallons
3. 0.75 gallons in l
4. 2.5 l in gallons
5. Estimate what 10 l will be in gallons

c) Use this centimetres and inches ruler to calculate the following:

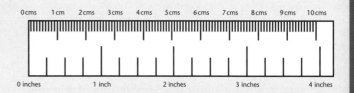

1. The number of mm in $\frac{1}{4}$ an inch.
2. The number of inches in 5.1 cm.
3. Estimate how many cm there are in 6 inches?
4. Estimate how many inches there are in 1 m?
5. How many mm in 1 inch?

Training Tips

Read scales carefully. Make sure you know what units you are writing down.

'Approximately' means 'about'. You don't have to be spot on but you need to be very close.

Perimeter

Perimeter is the distance around a 2-D shape.

> *Example*
> Perimeter = 44 cm + 22 cm + 44 cm + 22 cm
>   = 132 cm

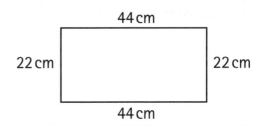

44 cm

22 cm   22 cm

44 cm

Bronze

a) Answer these questions:

1. A rectangle has a shortest side of 8 cm and a longest side of 12 cm. What is the perimeter?

2. The perimeter of a rectangle is 45 cm. The length of the longest side is 16 cm. What is the length of the shortest side?

3. The perimeter of a rectangle is 68 cm. The shortest side is 10 cm. What is the length of the longest side?

4. The perimeter of a rectangle is 82 m. The shortest side is 12 m. What is the length of the longest side?

5. The perimeter of a rectangle is 12 cm. The length of the longest side is 4 cm. What is the length of the shortest side?

6. A rectangle has a shortest side of 13 m and a longest side of 24 m. What is the perimeter?

7. The perimeter of a rectangle is 102 cm. The shortest side is 18 cm. What is the length of the longest side?

8. The perimeter of a rectangle is 161 cm. The length of the longest side is 65 cm. What is the length of the shortest side?

b) Measure the perimeter of these shapes using a ruler:

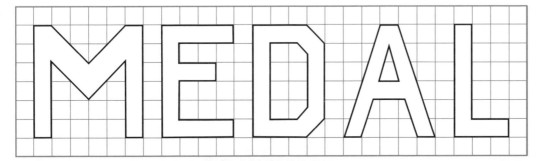

Training Tips

The formula for finding the perimeter of a rectangle is 'two times the length and breadth' or 2 x (l + b).

Training Tips

If a perimeter question has a missing side measurement, don't try to measure it with a ruler. The question wants to see if you can work it out from the measurements given.

Perimeter

Draw these shapes and write in the lengths you know. Work out the missing lengths (in units).
Now find the perimeter.

1.

4
?
5
?
2
8

2.
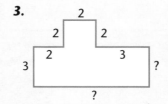
5
1
?
3
?
1

3.
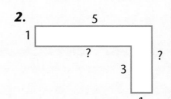
2
2
2
2
3
3
?
?

4.
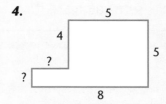
5
4
?
5
?
8

5.
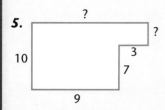
?
?
10
3
7
9

6.
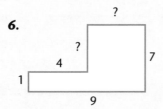
?
?
4
7
1
9

7.
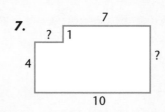
7
?
1
4
?
10

8.
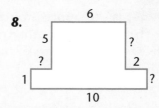
6
5
?
?
2
1
?
10

Draw these shapes and write in the lengths you know. Work out the missing lengths (in units).
Now find the perimeter.

1.

10
5
20
10
?
40
30
?

2.
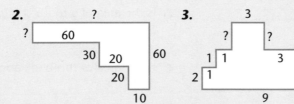
?
?
60
30
20
60
20
10

3.
3
?
?
1 1
3
?
2 1
1 ?
9

4.
5
5
2
2
3
1
?
?

5.
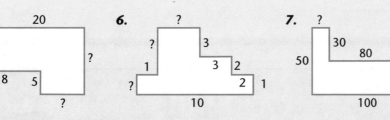
20
2
5
5
?
18
5
?

6.
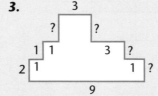
?
?
3
1
3
2
?
2
1
10

7.
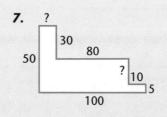
?
30
50
80
?
10
100
5

8.
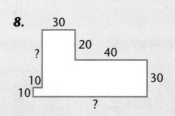
30
20
?
40
10
30
10
?

Area

Area is the space that is covered by a shape.

You can find the area of a right-angled triangle by turning it into a rectangle, finding the area of the rectangle and then halving your answer.

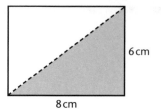

Area of this right-angled triangle = 24 cm²

> The formula for finding the area of a rectangle is
> **length × breadth or l × b**
> Make sure you learn it!

Bronze

a) What is the approximate area of these rectangles? Remember that these are scale drawings. Don't try to measure them – use the formula.

1.
2 cm
7 cm

2.
4 cm
8 cm

3.
18 mm
25 mm

4.
3 cm
13 cm

5.
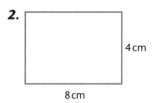
3.9 m
16.7 m

6.
5.4 m
45 m

7.
4.61 cm
17.2 cm

8.

1.1 cm
3.4 cm

9.
3.4 cm
15 cm

10.
5 mm
92 mm

b) Use your knowledge of area to answer these questions:

1. Would you expect the area of the classroom floor to be 4 m², 40 m² or 400 m²?

2. Would you expect the area of a postcard to be 8 cm², 80 cm² or 800 cm²?

3. Is the area of a football pitch about 5 m², 500 m² or 5000 m²?

4. Is the area of this book about 100 cm² 10 cm² or 600 cm²?

5. Which of these is more likely to be the area of a postage stamp? 150 mm², 1500 mm² or 10 mm².

Area

Silver

a) Find the area of these shapes. Split them into rectangles to help you.

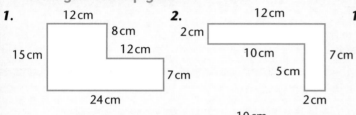
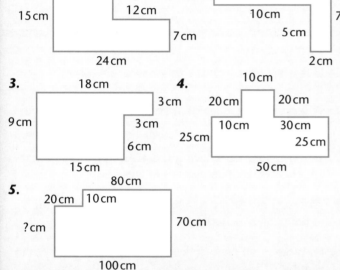

1.
12 cm
8 cm
12 cm
15 cm
7 cm
24 cm

2.
12 cm
2 cm
10 cm
7 cm
5 cm
2 cm

3.
18 cm
3 cm
9 cm
3 cm
6 cm
15 cm

4.
10 cm
20 cm   20 cm
10 cm   30 cm
25 cm   25 cm
50 cm

5.
80 cm
20 cm 10 cm
? cm   70 cm
100 cm

b) Use the information in the introduction to work out the area of these triangles:

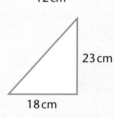

1.
5 cm
7 cm

2.
9 cm
12 cm

3.
8 cm
3.5 cm

4.
23 cm
18 cm

5.
4.6 cm
9.1 cm

Gold

a) Find the area of these shapes:

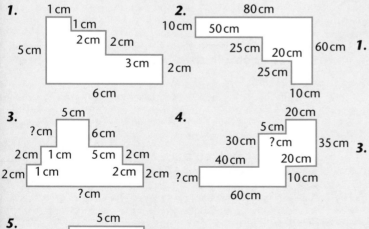

1.
1 cm
1 cm
2 cm   2 cm
5 cm
3 cm
6 cm

2.
80 cm
10 cm   50 cm
25 cm   20 cm   60 cm
2 cm   25 cm
10 cm

3.
5 cm
? cm   6 cm
2 cm 1 cm 5 cm 2 cm
2 cm 1 cm 2 cm 2 cm
? cm

4.
20 cm
5 cm
30 cm ? cm   35 cm
40 cm   20 cm
? cm   10 cm
60 cm

5.
5 cm
3 cm   1 cm
3 cm   2 cm
2 cm   4 cm
6 cm

b) Without using a calculator, find the total surface area of these cuboids. Remember each has 6 faces!

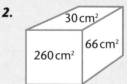
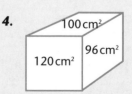

1.
80 cm²
56 cm²
10 cm²

2.
30 cm²
66 cm²
260 cm²

3.
3.5 m²
2.5 m²
1 m²

4.
100 cm²
96 cm²
120 cm²

5.
40 cm²
40 cm²
40 cm²

Time

Greenwich Mean Time (GMT) is the time measured from the Greenwich Royal Observatory in London. All other times in the world are either ahead of or behind GMT.

−10	−8	−6	−5	0	+1	+2	+3	+5	+7	+8	+9	+10	+12
Hawaii	Los Angeles	Chicago	New York	GMT	Rome	Istanbul	Kuwait	Delhi	Bangkok	Beijing	Tokyo	Canberra	Wellington
2:00	4:00	6:00	7:00	12:00 Midday	13:00	14:00	15:00	17:00	19:00	20:00	21:00	22:00	0:00

Bronze

a) At 13:00 in London, what time is it in these cities?

1. Kuwait

2. Tokyo

3. New York

4. Los Angeles

5. Bangkok

b) Use the world chart to answer these questions:

1. When the time is 14:30 in London, what time is it in Istanbul?

2. When children are having breakfast in London, what are children probably doing in Delhi?

3. When school finishes at 16:00 in Rome, are children in Bangkok at school?

4. If I wake up in New York at 8:00am, what time is it in Istanbul?

5. When children go to bed at 21:00 in Chicago, what time is it in London?

Silver

a) Use the world time chart to answer these questions:

1. When the time is 4:10 in London, what meal are people in Bejing eating?

2. When the time is 12:00 in Los Angeles, would any children be at school in England?

3. When school finishes at 15:30 in Istanbul, are schools likely to be open in Delhi?

4. If the time is midday in Canberra, what time is it in Hawaii?

5. If it is 7:22 in Wellington, what time is it in New York?

b) If it is midday in these places, what time is it in London?

1. Kuwait

2. Bangkok

3. Canberra

4. Chicago

5. Delhi

Time

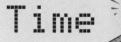

Gold

The Medal Maths airline flies to each of these destinations about four times a day. Copy and complete the timetable. Remember all times are local. The first row has been done for you.

London	Istanbul (+2hrs)	Delhi (+5hrs)	Beijing (+8hrs)	Canberra (+10hrs)	Los Angeles (−8hrs)	New York (−5hrs)
Flight time	**5hrs**	**7.5hrs**	**12hrs**	**24hrs**	**12hrs**	**7hrs**
08:00	15:00	20:30	04:00	18:00 (the next day!)	12:00	10:00
12:30					16:30	
16:00				02:00		
20:30		09:00				
21:45	04:45					
23:15						01:15

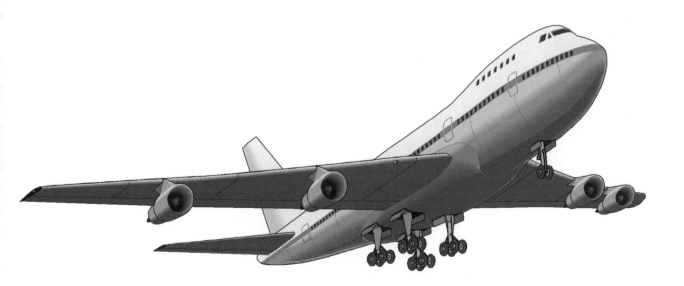

Training Tips

If your times go over the 24 hours then do the calculation in stages.

2-D shapes

2-D Shapes have corners and sides. They can also have parallel lines, equal sides, lines of symmetry and equal angles. Look at these examples.

 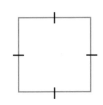 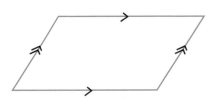 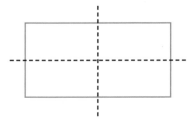

Bronze

a) Write the name of each of these shapes:

1.

2.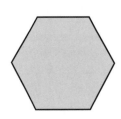

3.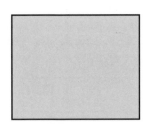

4.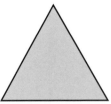

5.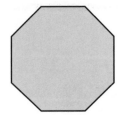

6.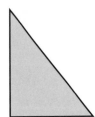

7.

8.

9.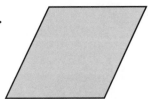

10.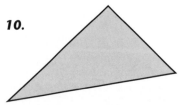

b) Write three properties of a rectangle.

c) Write two properties of an equilateral triangle.

d) Write three properties of a square.

Training Tips

Keep a note of the properties of different shapes. Include how many sides and whether each has parallel lines, equal sides or lines of symmetry.

2-D shapes

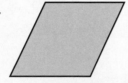
Silver

a) Name these shapes:

1.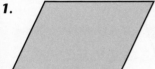

2.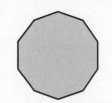

3.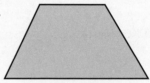

4.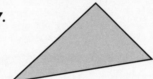

5.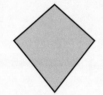

6.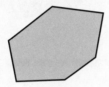

7.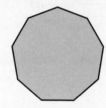

8.

9.

10.

b) Write a description of each of the shapes above next to its name. Remember to include the different properties.

Gold

a) Draw these shapes:

1. Parallelogram	**6.** Kite
2. Rhombus	**7.** Equilateral triangle
3. Square	**8.** Decagon
4. Rectangle	**9.** Scalene triangle
5. Trapezium	**10.** Right-angled triangle

b) Copy and complete this table by adding the names of the shapes above. Some may appear in more than one column.

Opposite sides that are parallel	2 equal sides	4 equal sides	2 equal angles	3 or more equal angles	Adjacent sides are equal	Diagonals bisect

Properties of 3-D shapes

3-D shapes are solid shapes.

This is an 'octahedron'.   This is a 'dodecahedron'.

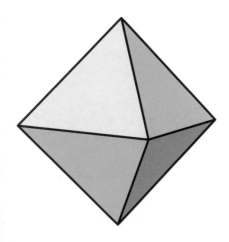

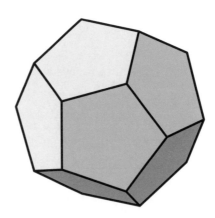

Bronze

Copy these shapes and name them:

1.

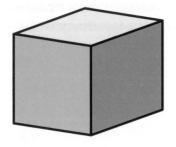

2.

3.

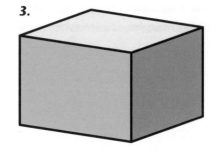

4.

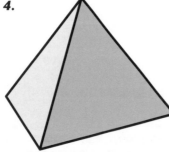

5.

 Keep a note of any names of shapes along with a sketch drawing. This will help you to remember them.

Properties of 3-D shapes

Copy each of these shapes and name them.
Next to the shape write the number of faces and edges.
Draw another shape with one more face than each of these.

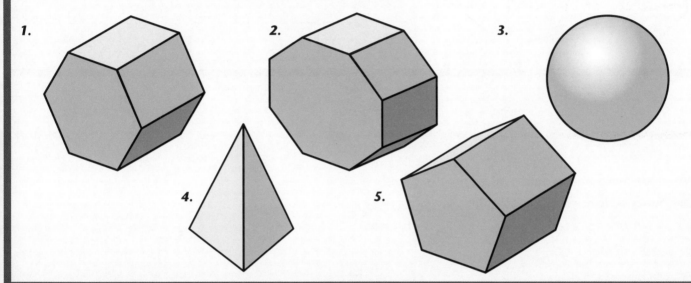

1.   **2.**   **3.**

4.   **5.**

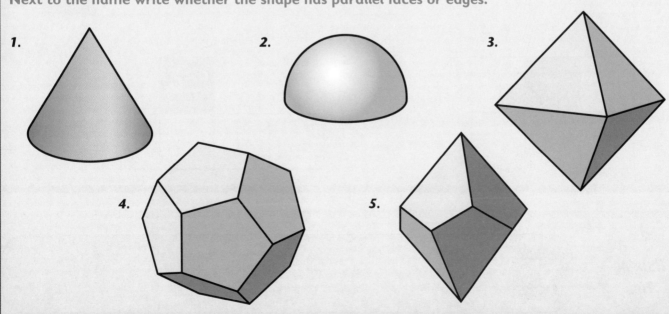

Copy each of these shapes and name them.
Next to the name write whether the shape has parallel faces or edges.

1.   **2.**   **3.**

4.   **5.**

Identifying nets of 3-D shapes

A net of a shape is what the 3-D shape would look like if it was 'flattened out'.
This box has a net that looks like this.

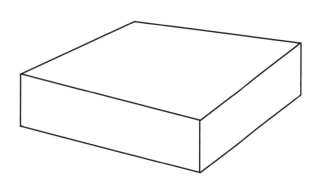

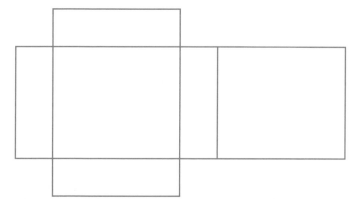

Which of these nets would make an open cube?
The black square shows each cube's base.

1.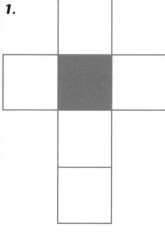

2.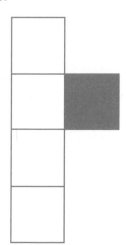

3.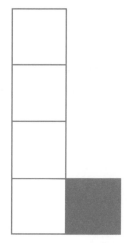

4.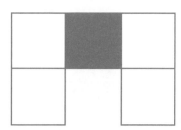

5.

Training Tips

You need to use your imagination when looking at nets.
Try to picture the shapes in your mind.

Identifying nets of 3-D shapes

Silver

Which of these nets would make a closed cube?

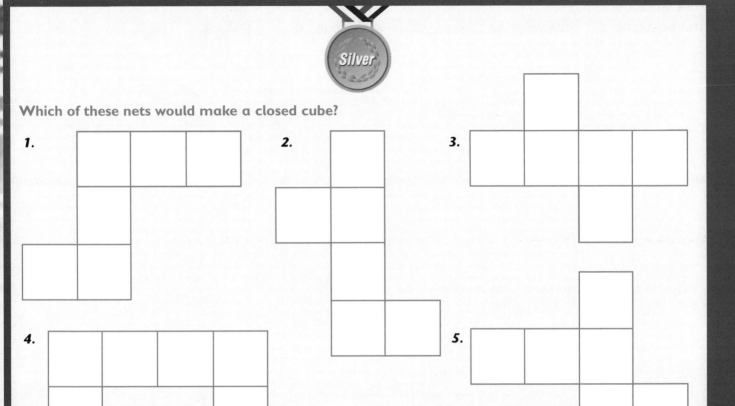

1.

2.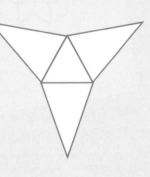

3.

4.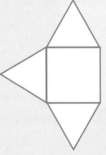

5.

Gold

Which of these nets would make a closed 3-D shape?

1.

2.

3.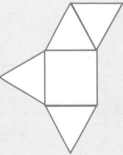

4.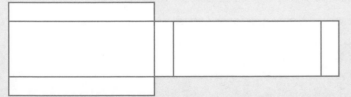

5.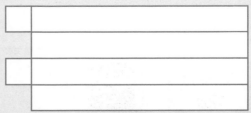

Visualising 3-D shapes from 2-D drawings

Look at this drawing.
You would need 8 more cubes to turn the shape into a cuboid.

Bronze

What is the least number of cubes needed to turn these shapes into cuboids?

1.

2.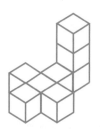

3.

4.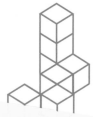

5.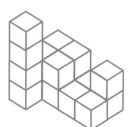

6.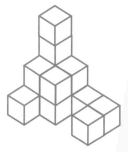

9.

10.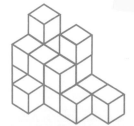

Training Tips

Work out the dimensions (length, breadth and height of the 3-D shape) to give you the total number of blocks needed to complete the shape. Subtract the number of cubes shown in the picture to give you the answer.

Visualising 3-D shapes from 2-D drawings

Silver

What is the least number of cubes needed to cover and join the shaded faces?

3.

GREEN
X 8

5.

Gold

What is the least number of cubes needed to cover and join the shaded faces?

1.

2.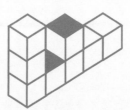

3.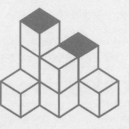

4.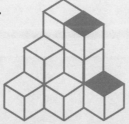

5.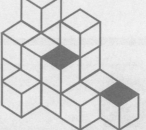

Reflective symmetry

Symmetry means a shape where two halves are a mirror image of each other.

line of symmetry or mirror line

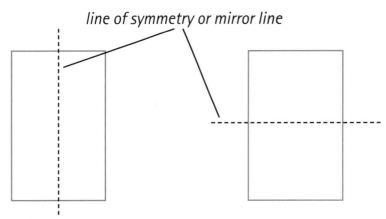

A rectangle has two lines of symmetry.

There are two places you could place a mirror to get an exact image of the rectangle.

You may find that using a small mirror can help in these questions.

Bronze

a) Draw these shapes. How many lines of symmetry are there in each shape?

1.

2.

3.

b) Complete these symmetrical patterns:

1.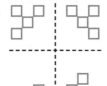

2.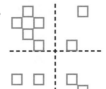

3.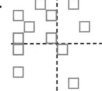

c) Sketch the reflection of these:

1.

2.

3.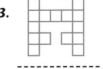

Training Tips

When completing patterns or translating shapes, complete the work step–by–step.

Reflective symmetry

Silver

a) Draw a shape with:

1. One line of symmetry   **2.** Two lines of symmetry   **3.** Three lines of symmetry

4. Four lines of symmetry   **5.** No lines of symmetry

b) Complete these symmetrical patterns in all four quadrants:

1.

2.
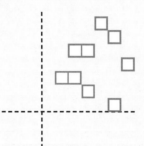

3.
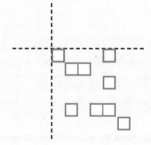

c) Sketch reflections for the following:

1.

2.

3.
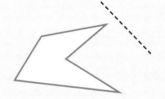

Gold

Copy these graphs and then translate each shape as follows:

1. 2 units to the left   **2.** 3 units down   **3.** 1 unit down   **4.** 3 units down and 1 to the right

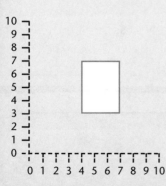

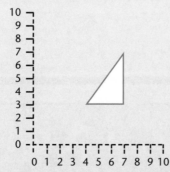

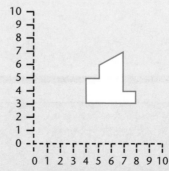

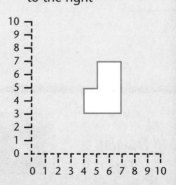

Position and direction

Key Facts

Perpendicular lines are at right angles to each other.

A diagonal is a straight line that joins the vertices of a polygon.

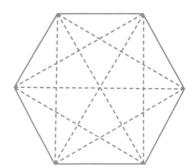

Parallel lines are the same distance apart – they never meet.

Two lines that cross each other are called intersecting lines. The point at which they cross is called an intersection.

Bronze

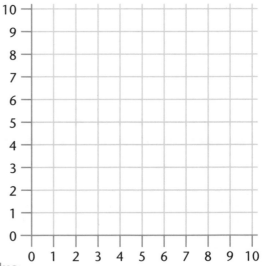

a) **Draw x and y axes on squared paper.**
   Now copy these shapes and answer the questions.

1. These points are the coordinates of the vertices of a shape: (2, 3) (2, 7) (4, 3) (4, 7). What is the name of the shape?

2. Three of the vertices of a square are (4, 1), (4, 3) and (6, 3). What are the coordinates of the 4th vertex?

3. Plot these coordinates: (4,2) (6, 2) (4, 5) (6, 5). What is the name of the shape?

4. Plot these coordinates: (1, 3) (3, 3) (1, 5) (3, 5) (2, 6). What is the name of the shape?

b) **Draw these shapes. Circle the perpendicular lines in blue.**
   Circle the parallel lines in red and draw in the diagonal lines
   (a straight line from a vertex to a non–adjacent vertex).

1.   **2.**   **3.**   **4.**   **5.**

Training Tips

The x axis is always read first, so go 'along the corridor, then up or down the stairs'.

The coordinates plot where the grid lines cross not the space in between them.

Position and direction

Silver

You will need to plot points in all four quadrants to answer these. Draw this on squared paper.

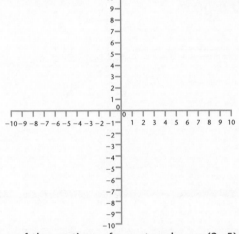

1. Three of the vertices of a rectangle are (3, 5), (7, 5) and (3, 9). What are the coordinates of the 4th vertex?

2. Plot these coordinates: (2, 6) (1, 5) (3, 5) (1, 3) (3, 3) (2, 2). What is the shape?

3. The points (−1, 1), (3, 5) and (−1, 5) are three of the four vertices of a square. What are the coordinates of the 4th vertex?

4. Draw a scalene triangle with each vertex in the second quadrant. Reflect the shape in the y axis and name the coordinates of each shape.

5. Plot these coordinates: (−3, 8) (2, 8) (−3, −2). What type of triangle is this?

6. Draw a square in the third and fourth quadrants. Reflect the shape in the x axis and name the coordinates of each shape.

7. What shape is this? (−2, 6) (−2, 0) (−4, −4) (0, 4)

8. Name this shape: (3, −6) (−2, −1) (−2, 4) (3, −1)

Gold

a) Draw these problems in four quadrants to help you get the answers.

1. Join these points to make a straight line: (−4, 4) and (−4, −2). Write the coordinates of two different points that you could join to make a parallel line.

2. Draw these two lines: (4, 2) (6, −4) and (8, 2) (2, −4). Write the coordinates where they intersect.

3. These three points lie in a straight line. Name three other points on this line: (−4, 6) (0, 2) (−5, 7).

4. Plot these coordinates: (2, 2) (2, −6) (−4, −6) (−4, 2). Name the shape. Where do the diagonals intersect?

b) Copy these shapes and then rotate them (clockwise) by the amount shown. Sketch the result and write the coordinates.

1. Rotate by 90 degrees.   **2.** Rotate by 180 degrees.

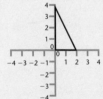   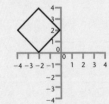

3. Rotate by 90 degrees.

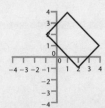

Angles
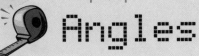

An angle less than 90 degrees is acute.

A right angle is 90 degrees.

An angle greater than 90 degrees and less than 180 degrees is obtuse.

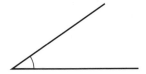

A reflex angle is greater than 180 degrees but less than 360 degrees.

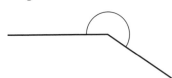

An angle of 180 degrees is a straight line.

Bronze

a) What type of angle are these?

1.

2.

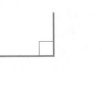

3.

4.

b) Estimate these angles:

1.

2.

3.

4.

c) Measure these angles:

1.

2.

3.

4.

Training Tips

The sum of all three angles inside a triangle is 180 degrees.
There are 360 degrees in a complete rotation.

Silver

a) Estimate and then measure these angles:

1.

2.

3.

4.

5.

b) Measure these angles:

1.

2.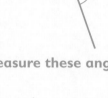

3.

4.

5.

c) Draw these angles:

1. 63°   **2.** 166°   **3.** 245°

4. 15°   **5.** 229°

Gold

a) Estimate and then measure these angles to the nearest degree:

1.

2.

3.

4.

5.

b) Draw these angles:

1. 179 degrees

2. 42 degrees

3. 86 degrees

4. 256 degrees

5. 345 degrees

c) Measure these angles to the nearest degree:

1.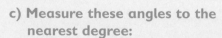

2.

3.

4.

5.

Angles in circles, triangles and straight lines

The total angles in a circle is 2 × 180° = 360°

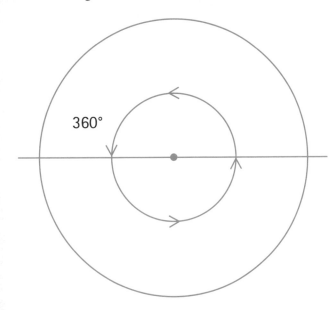

360°

The angles within a triangle always equal 180°.

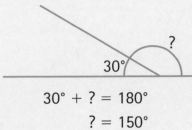

Example

?

75° 65°

75° + 65° + ? = 180°

? = 40°

Any angles on a straight line add up to 180°.

Example

?

30°

30° + ? = 180°

? = 150°

Bronze

a) Using the facts you have learnt, work out the missing angles:

1.
76° ?

2.
121° ?

3.
45° ?

4.
169° ?

5.
108° ?

6.
95° ?

7.
57° ?

b) Now work out these:

1.
? 80°
35°

2.
?
60° 75°

3.
?
70° 70°

4.
120° ?
10°

Training Tips

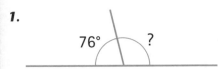
180 degrees = straight line or a half turn
360 degrees = a circle or a whole turn

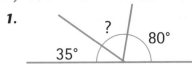
The angles of a triangle ALWAYS equal 180 degrees.

Angles in circles, triangles and straight lines

Silver

a) Find the missing angles:

1.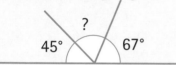
45° ? 67°

2.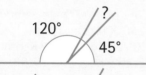
120° ? 45°

3.
60° ? 60°

4.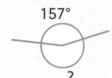
100° ? 40°

b) Find the missing angles:

1.
98° ?

2.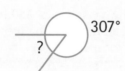
157° ?

3.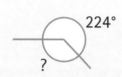
307° ?

4.
224° ?

c) Find the missing angles:

1.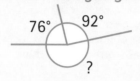
76° 92° ?

2.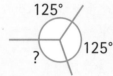
125° ? 125°

3.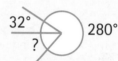
32° 280° ?

4.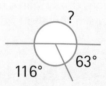
? 116° 63°

Gold

a) Find the missing angles:

1.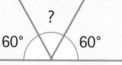
22° 222° ?

2.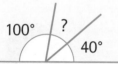
190° 33° ?

3.
90° 210° ?

4.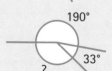
? 30° 300°

b) Find the missing angles:

1. & 2.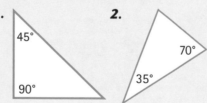
45° 90° 70° 35°

3. & 4.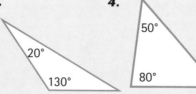
20° 130° 50° 80°

5.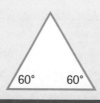
60° 60°

c) Now find these angles:

1. & 2.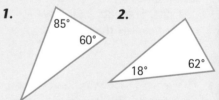
85° 60° 18° 62°

3. & 4.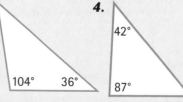
104° 36° 42° 87°

5.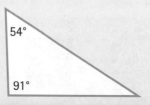
54° 91°

Single-step problems

Choose a suitable method and operation to answer these single-step 'real life' word problems.

Bronze

1. Three children play 'Monkey Ninjas from Hell' on their computer.
What did each child score?
Ewan: 426 + 105
Logan: 277 + 95
Isobelle: 392 + 141

2. Charlie's book has 358 pages. He starts from the beginning and reads 149 pages. How many more pages does Charlie have to read to reach the end of the book?

3. Jasmine has a pot of 622 peanuts. She eats 123. How many peanuts does Jasmine have left?

4. There are 1512 windows on the sky-scraper. The window cleaner has cleaned 463 of them. How many windows are still dirty?

Silver

1. 14 500 people bought 'Match-Stick Modelling Monthly' this year. That is 3842 more than last year. How many people bought 'Match-Stick Modelling Monthly' last year?

2. Bethany has a box of 350 beads to make bracelets. She uses 16 beads for each bracelet. How many bracelets can she make?

3. Neil and Rachel had a game of pinball. Neil scored 4490 points and Rachel scored 5998 points. How many more points than Neil did Rachel score?

4. A Jumbo Jet carries 227 passengers. How many passengers does a fleet of 15 Jumbos carry?

Gold

You can use a calculator or a written method to answer these.

1. The rap star 'Malt-Easer' has sold 250 000 copies of his album 'Cleaning Out My Bedroom'. Each album cost £7.99. How much did all the albums sell for?

2. Malt-Easer sells 300 000 copies of his second album for £9.99. How much did the albums sell for?

3. Rock group 'The Tightness' released their new album 'Squealing Trousers' – it sold 307 426 copies in one week. How many copies of 'Squealing Trousers' were sold on average per day?

4. The Tightness sold 156 294 albums fewer than a million during the next month. How many did they sell in that month?

Training Tips

Read the question, then read it again – what are the numbers you are dealing with and what do you have to do with them?

Single-step problems

Bronze

5. There are 46 cows in the field. How many legs are there?

6. Julie earns £4.60 from Mum for mowing the lawn and £3.57 from Dad for vacuuming the house. How much has Julie earned altogether?

7. There are 15 players in a rugby team. How many players are there in a league of 9 teams?

8. Stefan has 512 football stickers. There are 8 stickers in a pack. How many packs has Stefan bought?

9. 12 jam tarts fit on a plate. How many plates are needed to hold 108 jam tarts?

10. At the aquarium there are 846 tropical fish. The fish are divided equally into 6 tanks. How many fish are in each tank?

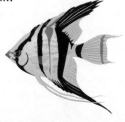

Silver

5. Gareth is saving up to buy a new super-computer which costs £2,199. He manages to save £3 per week. How many weeks will it take Gareth to save up enough to buy the computer?

6. There are 45 212 people at a football match. The following match there were 49 267 people at the game. How many people is that altogether?

7. There are 8995 chickens in the chicken shed. How many legs are there?

8. St Humpty Dumpty's school for accident prone children has 336 children and 16 padded classrooms. How many children are there in each class?

9. Stanley collects marbles. He has a bag which contains 4523. Stanley drops his bag and loses 1783 marbles. How many marbles does Stanley have left?

10. The explorer Sir Losten Found is aiming to be the first person to bounce to the South Pole on a pogo stick. He manages 6300 bounces in a day. How many bounces will he do in 14 days?

Gold

5. Malt-Easer sold 672 098 albums and The Tightness sold 934 933 albums. How many more albums did The Tightness sell?

6. A new group called Fussy is trying to launch their first album "I'm Fussy". They want to sell their albums at £6.99. If they sell 345 240 copies in total, how much will they make?

7. At the Rock Festival, The Tightness, Malt–Easer and Fussy play to a packed crowd. There are 73 251 in the audience. If each paid £25 to get in, how much did the concert raise.

8. Another 12 394 people came in free as friends of the bands. How much did the organisers miss out on by letting these people in for free?

9. T–Shirts sell well at the concert. At £15 each the total made was £443 385. How many T–shirts were sold?

10. If each band sold the same number of T–shirts, how many did each band sell?

 **Training Tips**

 Remember to check your answers. Do they look correct? Have you answered the question?

Multi-step problems

These questions require you to perform two, three or maybe four steps in order to get them right!

Bronze

1. Grant and Phil are selling penny sweets. They started with 1900. Grant sells 365 and Phil sells 773. How many sweets are left?

2. Jack and Joanna are selling clothes from a market stall. Jack sells £87 worth and Joanna sells £104 worth. They spend £50 on new stock. How much profit have they made?

3. Jenny buys 6 strips of raffle tickets and Jessica buys 5 strips. The raffle tickets cost 75p a strip. How much do they spend on raffle tickets altogether?

4. Stanley has read 156 of the 620 pages of his book 'Ten Thousand Miles in the Saddle' (by Ivor Rawbottom). How many more pages must Stanley read to reach the middle?

5. Charlotte thinks of a number. She subtracts 24 and divides it by 8. The answer is 20. What number was Charlotte thinking of?

Silver

1. Louise has been given 100 football stickers. She gives a fifth of them to Hannah, a quarter of the remainder to Ryan and 26 to Jamie. How many stickers does Louise have left?

2. Ali bought three CDs for £15.99 each. His brother bought another two CDs at £13.99 each. How much did they spend together?

3. Each week Kim saves $\frac{1}{2}$ of her pocket money for a DVD player. If it takes her 30 weeks to save the £75 she needs for the player, how much is her pocket money per week?

4. There are 96 pages in this book. If there is an average of 45 questions on each page, how many questions do you need to complete to do half the book?

5. At the school disco there 3 boys dancing for every 2 girls. There are 28 girls dancing. How many boys were dancing?

Gold

1. 1860 doughnuts are put into bags. Two thirds are put into red bags and half of the rest are put into blue bags. The remaining doughnuts are put into green bags. How many doughnuts were in the blue bags?

2. The TV show 'Big Bore Brother' is watched by 6 000 006 people. However $\frac{2}{3}$ of them are asleep and a $\frac{1}{6}$ are reading a book. The rest are actually taking notice. How many viewers are really reading a book?

3. At Farnaby Road School there are 300 pupils. 55% have packed lunch and 45% have school dinners. On Tuesday seven children are absent. If 2 of these children have packed lunch, how many school dinners are needed?

4. Another TV show, 'Maths Idol', is watched by 45 938 on the opening night. This increased by 10% per day until the grand final 5 days later. How many watched on the third day?

5. Fiddlesticks United score an average of 4 goals in their 15 league games. If 3 games were scoreless and Fiddlesticks scored 6 goals in 8 games, how many goals did they score in their last 4 games?

Training Tips

Once you have established the numbers you are calculating, estimate an answer of the calculation.

Multi-step problems

Bronze

Silver

Gold

Alexa is going to walk from Lands End to John O'Groats. She has got to walk 1086 miles!

6. When she has travelled 150 miles, how far will it be until she is halfway?

7. If she walks 14 miles a day for 70 days, how much further will she have to travel?

8. Alexa has a budget of £20 per day to spend on food and accommodation. Walking at 15 miles a day, how much will she need to take with her?

9. Alexa hopes to raise £5750 from her walk. If she gets one big sponsor for £2000, how much more will she need to raise per mile to reach her target?

10. Alexa finished the walk. It took her 73 days and 4 hours! If she walked 12 miles in the last 4 hours, how far did she walk on average for the other 73 days?

Kamal and Andy are saving pocket money to go to France to visit their pen friends. They are also hoping to raise money by selling their old Sprocket stickers. The stickers sell at £0.25p each.

6. If they need £150 and hope to save £35 each from pocket money, how many stickers do they need to sell each to get to their target?

7. Kamal has a birthday and gets £20 from an aunt. He also gets 20 stickers. How much has he raised?

8. The boys decide to take an extra £25 to buy presents for their families. If they use £10 of their pocket money, how much will they need to make from stickers?

9. Their last 300 stickers are sold in a sale at £0.15p. How much extra could they have made if they sold them at full price?

10. At the end of their visit to France the boys decide to meet their pen friends in London when they come next year. If their trip to London will cost £45 each, how many full price stickers will they need to sell in total to make the trip?

Use a calculator and your rounding skills for these questions.

Rising Stars Bank Interest Rates on Savings:

£0–100	5% per annum
£101–£500	6% per annum
£501+	7% per annum

6. Sanjay saves £90 in his first year and makes £4.50 interest. In the second year he saves a further £200. What is the total in his account at the end of the second year?

7. Sanjay has £600 in the bank at the top rate of interest, how much will the account be worth in 2 years time?

8. If Sanjay takes £40 out of his account leaving £560, how much will the account be worth over the same 2 years?

9. If Sanjay saves for 5 years he gets a bonus payment of 10% of the final balance. If he saves £560 for 5 years, what is his final balance?

10. Sanjay's younger sister puts £1 into a Rising Stars bank account. If she leaves it there, how much will she have after 5 years? (Don't forget the bonus payment!)

Training Tips

Scan the questions for important words and phrases such as 'How many' or 'Who' and 'What'.

Shopping problems

Solve these problems which are all about money and shopping bills. Learning to handle and deal with money is a very useful life-skill.

Bronze

1. What change do you get from £20 for a CD costing £13.99?

2. Find the total of these bills from the baker's shop – 76p, 93p, 58p and £4.75.

3. Petrol costs 72.6p per litre. How much does it cost fill the tank of a scooter which holds 10 litres?

4. Ross buys 5 magazines for £2.75 each. How much does he spend altogether?

5. How much change from £50 do you get for a pair of shoes costing £27.95?

Silver

1. What change from £50 would you get if you bought a football shirt for £29.99, some shorts for £9.99 and some socks for £5.99?

2. What is the cost of 335 text messages at 3p each?

3. You can buy 5 cans of 'Burpsi' for £1.85. How much does one can cost?

4. Jeff has £100. He spends £24.50 on a necklace for his girlfriend, £41.78 on a meal for two and gives £12 to his younger brother for babysitting. How much does Jeff have left?

5. What is the cost in pounds of a bus ride each week for a year at 70p a ride?

Gold

1. What is the total of these supermarket bills? £104.52, £178.23, £42.89 and £29.91.

2. A burger van sells 4925 burgers at £1.35 each. What is the total cost of the burgers?

3. 8692 people pay £8.25 to visit a theme park. How much is paid in total?

4. James wins £1 000 000 on the lottery! He gives £762.50 to the local home for lost cats and spends the rest on sweets. How much does James spend on sweets?

5. Ravi spends £15.92 on CD singles. If each one costs £1.99, how many singles has he bought?

Training Tips

Next time you are at the supermarket, as the goods are being scanned, see if you can mentally add the shopping bill! Make it easier by rounding items up or down to the nearest pound. See how close you are to the final bill.

Shopping problems

Bronze

Silver

Gold

Supermarket prices

Soap	£0.76p
Butter	£1.25
Chicken	£4.55
Soup	£0.54p
Carrots (500g)	£2.24
Tomatoes (500g)	£1.89
Apple juice (1l)	£0.74p
Orange juice (1l)	£1.01p

6. How much does soup, chicken and two litres of orange juice cost?

7. If Calum buys two bars of soap and a bag of carrots, how much does he need to spend?

8. Calum gives the shop assistant a £10 note. How much change should he get?

9. Maggie has £5.00 and buys a carton of apple juice, a packet of butter and a tin of tomatoes. How much change should she get?

10. James buys 4 tins of soup and a carton of orange juice. How much does he spend?

Txt Fun

Text message prices

First 500 messages 3p each

Next 500 messages 2.5p each

Further messages 2p each

6. Harriet sends 750 text messages in a year. How much does she spend on texting?

7. James only sends 583 messages. How much is his bill?

8. Katy 1029 messages. How much does she spend?

9. Use the prices above. If all the children's messages were sent from one phone, what would the cost be?

10. The next year the three friends send 10% fewer messages. How much did they each spend?

Melissa goes shopping with a £50 note and a £20 note. In the first shop she spends £12.56 on a DVD, £10.99 on a book and £9.98 on a CD. In the second shop she buys a pair of shoes for £17.99 and some shoe polish for £2.50.

6. How much does she spend in the first shop?

7. How much change would she get from the £50 note?

8. How much does she spend in the second shop?

9. If she spends the £20 note in the second shop, how much change will she get?

10. Investigate the different notes and coins that Melissa might be left with at the end of her shopping trip.

Training Tips

Scan the questions for important words and phrases such as 'How many' or 'Who' and 'What'.

Converting foreign currency

If you go abroad you will probably have to change your money into a different currency. This can be confusing! How do you know how much you have and what you are spending?

 Bronze

Look at this exchange rate at the bank.

> £1 = 1.7 US Dollars
> 2.4 Australian Dollars
> 10.6 South African Rand
> 184 Japanese Yen

1. How many US Dollars can I have for £2?

2. How many Australian Dollars can I have for £4?

3. How many Yen are there in £27.50?

4. I have 106 Rand. How much is this worth in pounds?

5. If I take £100 spending money on holiday to Florida, how many dollars will I have?

 **Silver**

There are 1.35 Euros to £1.

1. What is the price in pounds of a car costing 15 400 Euros?

2. What is the price in Euros of a Plasma screen TV costing £3500?

3. If I have 1350 Euros, how much is this worth in pounds?

4. If I take £550 to spend in Italy, how many Euros will I exchange it for?

5. John pays 28 000 Euros for a new car in France. How many pounds would it have cost in England?

 **Gold**

There are 1818 South Korean Won to £1.

1. If you had 1 818 000 Won, how many pounds would that be?

2. A flat costs £89 000. How much is that in South Korean Won?

3. Frankie earns £27 500 in a year. How much is that in Won?

4. How many Won is 1p worth?

5. Juan wins 100 000 Won on one wonderful game of one-on-one basketball. How many pounds has Juan won?

 Training Tips

Foreign exchange rates change daily. Find out how much a Euro is worth today. Look in a newspaper or on the Internet.

Converting foreign currency

Bronze

Silver

Gold

Bronze

6. I send £50 to my aunt in Australia. How many dollars can she exchange it for?

7. Which is worth the most in pounds? A hundred Rand or a hundred US Dollars?

8. How many yen can I have for £1000?

9. How many Yen is 25p worth?

10. What is the cost in US Dollars of a new computer costing £600?

Silver

Use a calculator or a written method for these.
There are 85 Indian Rupees to £1
There are 96 Jamaican Dollars to £1

6. Find the price in Rupees of a house costing £105000.

7. Find the price in Jamaican Dollars of a house costing £129000.

8. Find the price in Rupees of a car costing £19999.

9. How many Jamaican Dollars does a new motorbike cost if it is priced at £1750?

10. Which costs more in pounds and by how much – a DVD costing 850 rupees or a CD costing 864 Jamaican Dollars?

Gold

In Cyprus there are 0.77 Cypriot pounds to £1.

6. A bike costs £99. How much is that in Cypriot pounds?

7. A games console costs 120 Cypriot pounds. How much is that in £?

8. How many Cypriot pounds is Ali's £50 savings worth?

9. Layla earns 436 Cypriot pounds in her delicatessen. How much is that worth in pounds sterling?

10. Cem finds £2.50 in his pocket. How much is that in Cypriot pounds?

Training Tips

1.35 Euros *to* a pound means that one pound *is worth* or is *the same as* 1.35 Euros.

Calculating fractions and percentages

Remember your fraction/percentage equivalents (see page 20).
They will help you answer these questions.

Bronze

a) There is a 10% discount at the sports shop. How much is the discount on the following?

1. A £200 set of golf clubs

2. A £25 tennis racket

3. A £66 pair of trainers

4. A £48 cricket bat

5. A £110 croquet set

b) The agent's fee for securing sponsorship deals for a top Premiership footballer is 5%. Calculate the fee on these deals:

1. A £70 000 boot deal

2. A £120 000 shirt endorsement

3. £68 000 for promoting aftershave

4. A £83 000 mobile phone promotion

5. A £180 000 launch of a new range of underpants

c) When a player is sold an agent can get up to 20% of the transfer fee. Calculate the fees on these deals:

1. 7% of £150 000

2. 10% of £1 000 500

3. 15% of £3 333 333

4. 17.5% of £8 567 000

5. 20% of £18 350 235

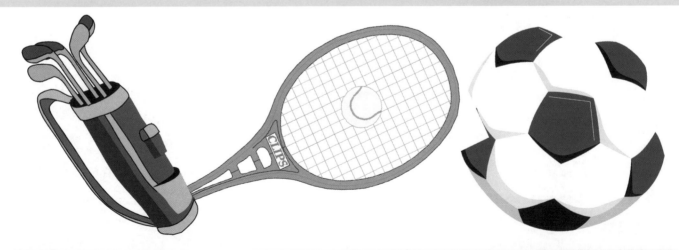

Training Tips

To find **0.5%** – first find **10%** then **10%** of that and then halve your answer.
e.g **0.5% of £60 = £6** then **60p** then **30p**

Calculating fractions and percentages

Remember your fraction/percentage equivalents (see page 20).
They will help you answer these questions.

Silver

1. Work out how much I save if I buy a £6 pair of shorts at 10% discount.

2. How much would I save on a football if the price drops by 10% from £9.00?

3. The deposit on a £260 rowing machine is 50%. How much is the deposit?

4. There is a 'buy one get one half price' promotion on hockey sticks. The sticks are £8. If I buy two, how much will I spend?

5. The sports shop has an 'everything for half price' day. How much is a snooker cue sold for on half price day if it normally sells for £39.98?

6. A tennis racket is reduced by 10% from its original price of £22. What is the new price of the tennis racket?

7. Footballs have increased in price by 10% after the cup final. How much would a football cost that used to be £9.00?

8. A new track-suit costs £36. There is 25% off in the sale. How much does it cost now?

9. Tennis balls are £5 for 4 with a 15% reduction in the sale. What is the sale price of 4 tennis balls?

10. Socks are 20% off for a week. How much do 3 pairs cost in the sale if they are normally £5.00?

Gold

a) Ticket prices for the next Olympics have been cut by $17\frac{1}{2}$%!
   How much will these seats cost now?

1. Upper tier block 34 – £35

2. Lower tier block 4 – £55

3. Track-side – £110

4. Upper box – £125

5. Lower box – £225

b) The agent's fee for negotiating sponsorship has now gone up to $12\frac{1}{2}$%!
   What are the fees for these deals?

1. Promoting a sport drink – £25 000

2. Modelling underpants – £45 000

3. Appearing on the cover of FIFA 2006 video game – £95 000

4. Selling small French cars on TV – £250 000

5. Promoting bad eating habits with McChubbies burgers – £500 000

c) Work out the final price of these items, including the percentage increase or decrease:

1. A sports drink at £1.99 reduced by 15%

2. A football at £9.99 increased by 25%

3. A pair of socks at £4.99 reduced by 8%

4. A tracksuit at £15.99 reduced by 12%

5. A pair of boots at £25.99 increased by 17.5%

Training Tips

Practise working out discounts when you are at the shops.
Compare deals and prices as you go.

Problems involving length

These are 'story' problems involving kilometres, metres, centimetres and millimetres.
Remember which units the questions are using (km, m, cm, mm).

Bronze

1. James jumped 145 cm in the long jump. Carl's final jump was 4 cm less. How far did Carl jump?

2. Priya ran 1200 m. Stephen ran ½ as far. How far did he run?

3. Dave runs 12 times around the track to raise money for his school. Once around the track is 400 m. How many metres does Dave run in total?

4. Carl jumped 138 cm and 127 cm in the long jump. How far did he jump in metres altogether?

5. Sasha threw the javelin 63 cm further than Sabrina who threw it 12.25 m. How far did Sasha throw the javelin?

Silver

1. In the 10000 m race, Harpreet has run 5 laps of 400 m. How many metres has Harpreet still got to run?

2. Greg has completed ¾ of the 20 km cycle race. How many metres has he left to go?

3. How many centimetres are covered from start to finish by eight athletes running the 100 m?

4. Leo jumped 1.98 m, Finley jumped 2.79 m and Jamie jumped 63 cm less than Finley. What is the total distance of all three long jumps?

5. Wesley threw a cricket ball 720 mm further than Joseph who threw it 58.23 m. How many metres did Wesley throw the cricket ball?

Gold

1. Lyndsey jumped 6 mm further than Alice who jumped 7.5 cm less than Jenny. Jenny jumped 1.45 m. How far did Lyndsey jump?

2. How many millimetres does an athlete run if they complete the 10000 m?

3. How many centimetres do all 8 teams cover when they race the 4 x 100 m relay?

4. How many centimetres do all 8 teams cover when they race the 4 x 400 m relay?

5. The distances for 4 javelin throws were as follows: 45.36 m, 73.51 m, 78.77 m and 72.62 m. What was the total distance in centimetres?

Training Tips

 Remember 10 mm = 1 cm, 100 cm = 1 m and 1000 m = 1 km.

Problems involving length

Bronze

6. Cathy jumps 113 cm in the high jump. That is 40 mm more than Jessie. How high in cm does Jessie jump?

7. Zoe ran three and a half times further than Claire who ran 1500 m. How far did Zoe run?

8. Mr Quick the PE teacher could do the 100 m in 25 seconds but Stephanie was 50% quicker. How long did it take Stephanie to run the 100 m?

9. Erin has run $\frac{1}{4}$ of a 200 m race. How far has she still got to run?

10. Meena threw the javelin 10 m. Jane threw it 10% less. How far did Jane throw the javelin?

Silver

6. Jason threw the cricket ball 1215 mm past the end of the tape measure. If the tape measure was 60 m, how far did Jason throw the cricket ball?

7. Sofie has run 25% of the 800 m race. How far has she got to go?

8. Finn has run the 100 m, 200 m and 400 m. How many centimetres has he run so far.

9. If Finn now runs the 1500 m, how many centimetres will he have run in total?

10. Lloyd jumped 2.04 m, then 1.85 m and then 1.92 m. What is the distance between his longest and shortest jumps?

Gold

6. Kofi has run 18% of the 400 m race. How far has he got to go now?

7. The high jump was won by Joanne with a jump of 1.56 m. The second place jump was 32 mm less. How high did the second jumper jump?

8. Jack ran in the 800 m, the 1500 m and the 10 000 m. How many kilometres did he run?

9. Rachel threw the javelin 40 metres. If Sam threw the javelin 6.34 m less than Rachel but the same as Peter who threw it 38.35 m, how far was Rachel's throw?

10. Ben didn't finish any of his races but ran 30% of the 100 m, 25% of the 400 m and $\frac{1}{5}$ of the 1500 m. How far did he run in total?

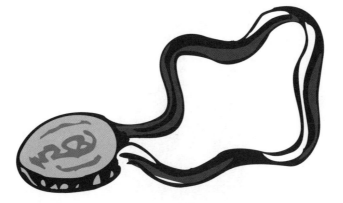

Training Tips

Check your answers and the units you have used. Would 120 m be a sensible answer for how far Leo jumped in the high jump? No, but 120 cm would be.

Problems involving mass

These are 'story' problems involving kilograms (kg) and grams (g).

Bronze

1. A weightlifter lifts 48 kg more than his opponent who lifts 165 kg. How much does the weightlifter lift?

2. David lifts 6500 g more than Martin who lifts 170 kg. How many kg does David lift?

3. My sports bag weighs 2 kg. If I take out my running shoes it weighs 400 g less. How much does my sports bag weigh now?

4. Martin lifts 173 kg and David lifts 31 kg more. How many kg does David lift?

5. Martin trains hard for a month. He lifts 210 kg! David lifts 920 g less. How many kg does David lift now?

Silver

1. The wrestler 'Puny Pete' is 300 g heavier than 'Nerdy Nigel' who is 48.90 kg. How heavy is 'Puny Pete' in kg?

2. Steve's football boots weigh 760 g each. How much do the two boots weigh together?

3. James has 2.56 kg of sweets to sell. If he manages to get rid of 1.02 kg of sweets, how much is left?

4. How many grams of horse feed must be added to 2.73 kg to make 5 kg of horse feed altogether?

5. How many grams of sugar will I need to make a super smoothie for 8 people if one smoothie requires 45 grams?

Gold

1. What is the difference in grams between a bike that weighs 11.78 kg and a cyclist that weighs 73.9 kg?

2. What is the difference in kg between a boxer who weighs 91 585 g and one who weighs 89.6 kg?

3. Johnny weighs 73.451 kg and Alex weighs 62.1 kg. What is the difference in grams?

4. Bruce the potter has a lump of clay that weighs 309 kg. Each pot that Bruce makes needs 120 g of clay. How many pots can Bruce make from his lump of clay?

5. Brian the builder has 3.69 kg of nails in his toolbox. If he uses 35 nails and has 0.54 kg of nails left, how much does each nail weigh?

 **Training Tips**

 Remember – 1000 g = 1 kg

 Adding the zero to decimal numbers can help when you are dealing with numbers to 3 decimal places, e.g. 56.4 kg is actually 56 kg and 400 g.

Problems involving capacity

These are 'story' problems involving litres (l), millilitres (ml) and centilitres (cl).

Bronze

1. A runner drinks 345 ml of water straight after a race and another 470 ml a little later. How many ml of water has the runner drunk altogether?

2. A car holds 50 litres of petrol. A van holds three and a half times as much. How many litres of petrol can the van hold?

3. How many 250 ml jugs of water are needed to fill a bowl which holds 6 litres?

4. If Peter has a bottle of drink which contains 330 cl, how many centilitres will he have left if he drinks 175 cl?

5. How many litres of juice are there in 6 cartons – with each carton containing 500 ml?

Silver

1. Wendy uses 25 oranges to make $1\frac{1}{4}$ litres of orange juice. How many litres of orange juice can she make with 75 oranges?

2. A container full of orange juice holds 4.2 litres. A full jug holds 200 ml of orange juice. How many full jugs will it take to fill the container?

3. A container which holds 7.8 litres of cola is knocked over. 1.9 litres is spilt. How many litres of cola are left in the container?

4. Kerry has 6 cups of tea each day. Each cup holds 275 ml of tea. How much tea does Kerry drink each day?

5. Charlie has 20,000 cl of water in his garden pond. How many litres is that?

Gold

1. A drinks stand sells 623 cans of 'Burpsi' in a day. Each can holds 330 ml. How many litres of Burpsi are sold?

2. If the stand sells 5000 cans containing 330 ml of Burpsi in a week, how many litres is that?

3. A supermarket sells 6241 pots of fresh soup in a week. Each pot contains 750 ml. How many litres of soup is that?

4. The least popular soup in the supermarket is 'Offal Broth' which sells 26 pots of 750 ml each week. The most popular soup is 'Cream of Chocolate' which sells 4,396 pots of 750 ml. What is the difference in litres?

5. A lorry which delivers soup holds 7000 pots, each pot containing 750 ml. However, the lorry overturns on the motorway and 5113 pots of soup are smashed (causing a 'souper' explosion!). How many litres of soup are left?

 **Training Tips**

Remember – 10 ml = 1 cl
1000 ml = 1 litre
100 cl = 1 litre

Try to picture measures in your head. 1 litre is a large carton of fruit juice.

Problems involving imperial measures

The Imperial system is the old system of measurement. We mainly use the metric system but it very useful to be able to convert units of one system to the units of the other.

Use this conversion table to help you answer these questions.

Imperial to Metric	Metric to Imperial
1 mile = 1.61 km	1 km = 0.62 mile
1 yard (36 inches) = 91.4 cm	1 m = 39 inches
1 foot = 30.5 cm	1 cm = 0.39 inch
1 inch = 2.54 cm	1 l = 1.76 pts
1 gallon = 4.55 l	1 g = 0.04 oz
1 pint = 0.57 l	1 kg = 2.20 lb
1 pound = 0.45 kg	
1 ounce = 28.35 g	

Bronze

1. How long in centimetres is a 10 inch photo-frame?

2. How heavy in pounds is a suitcase weighing 5 kg?

3. How many litres of petrol are there in a tank which contains 10 gallons?

4. How many yards are there in 400 metres?

5. How many pints are there in 10 litres?

Silver

1. How many centimetres does Jimmy win the race by if he wins by a yard?

2. The 1500 m race is run over how many yards?

3. The 5000 m race is run over how many yards?

4. My Dad is 5 feet and 10 inches tall. How tall is this in centimetres?

5. My Dad weighs 12 stone. How heavy is this in kilograms and grams?

Gold

1. A champion javelin thrower throws the javelin 90 m. How many inches is that?

2. Mount Everest is 29 028 feet tall. How tall is this to the nearest metre?

3. The River Nile is the longest river in the world. It stretches 3 900 miles. How far is this in kilometres?

4. How far is this in yards?

5. How far is this in inches?

Training Tips

Most distances on road signs in the United Kingdom are measured in miles. Next time you are on a car journey, see if you can convert a road sign into kilometres.

Problems involving imperial measures

Bronze

6. What is 12 feet in metres?

7. If I run 2.5 miles, how many kilometres is that?

8. My book weighs about 250 g. How many ounces is that?

9. If I drink 2 litres of water, how many pints is this?

10. I am 157 centimetres tall. Am I closer to 4 ft or 5 ft?

Silver

Pancake Ingredients
100 g flour
200 ml milk
100 ml water
1 egg
50 g butter

6. How many ounces of flour do I need to make these pancakes?

7. How much liquid am I adding to the flour, in pints?

8. Do I need more or less than 2 ounces of butter for this recipe?

9. If I double the recipe how many millilitres of liquid will I need?

10. How much flour in ounces will I need for the doubled recipe?

Gold

Scone Ingredients
(makes 10 scones)
250 g flour
50 g caster sugar
125 ml milk

6. How many ounces of dry ingredients will I need to make this recipe?

7. My mixing jug is only in Imperial measures. How many pints of milk will I need?

8. I want to make the mixture sweeter. If I add another ounce of sugar, how many ounces will there be in total?

9. I want to make 15 scones. How many grams of flour will I need?

10. How many ounces of sugar will I need for the 15 scones?

Training Tips

'A metre is just 3 feet 3. It's longer than a yard you see!'

Problems involving time

These 'story' problems are about time. 'Counting on' can be a useful way of solving them.

Bronze

1. The women's marathon started at 08:30 and finished at 10:57. How long did the race last?

2. The men's marathon started at 12:55 and lasted for 2 hours and eight minutes. At what time did it finish?

3. Four runners in the school 4 x 400m relay run the following times: 84.2 seconds, 89.5 seconds, 93.7 seconds and 77.7 seconds. What is the total time in minutes for all four runners?

4. Mike ran the 100m in 13.63 seconds. Neil came second and was 1.72 seconds slower. What was Neil's time for the 100m?

5. Diane swam 200m in 7 minutes and 25 seconds. She swam a further 300m in 10 minutes and 56 seconds. What was her total time taken to swim 500m?

6. Next year's sports day will take place 362 days after this year's. If this year's sports day took place on 5th July, what day will next year's be on? Next year is not a leap year.

7. The Olympics takes place over 28 days. If it starts on the 28th of July, when will it end?

The longest marathon was run by Lloyd Scott (in a diving costume). It took him six days, four hours, 30 minutes and 56 seconds to complete the Edinburgh Marathon in 2003.

8. How long is this in hours?

9. How long is this in minutes?

10. How long is this in seconds?

Training Tips

When counting days in years etc. don't forget the leap years, which have February 29th as an extra day. Olympic years are leap years – 2004, 2000, 1996, 1992...

Problems involving time

These 'story' problems are about time. 'Counting on' can be a useful way of solving them.

Silver

This is a table showing the cooking times for different types of meat.
Copy and complete the table.

Kilograms/ Cooking Times	1 kg	1.5 kg	2 kg	2.5 kg	3 kg	3.5 kg
Chicken (45 mins per kg + 20 mins.)						
Beef (55 mins per kg + 20 mins)						
Pork (66 mins per kg + 35 mins)						
Lamb (50 mins per kg + 25 mins)						
Mutton (88 mins per kg + 15 mins)						

Gold

1. The runner Paula Radcliffe's birthday is on December 17th. How many days ago was it from today?

2. How many months have you been alive?

3. How many weeks have you been alive?

4. How many days have you been alive?

5. How many weeks until your 100th birthday?

6. If you were born in 1998 and lived to be 104, how many centuries would you have lived in?

7. My brother was born in 2001. If his birthday was on December 6th, on what day was he 1000 days old?

How many seconds:
8. In a football match?
9. In a week?
10. Do you spend at school each day?

Training Tips

60 seconds = 1 minute   60 minutes = 1 hour
24 hours = 1 day   7 days = 1 week
52 weeks = 1 year   12 months = 1 year   10 years = a decade

Frequency bar charts

Graphs are an excellent way to show what data looks like.
Bar charts or bar line charts are easier to read than looking at
lots of numbers.

Bronze

This frequency bar chart shows the number of pets owned by the children in 'Timber-Wolf' Class.

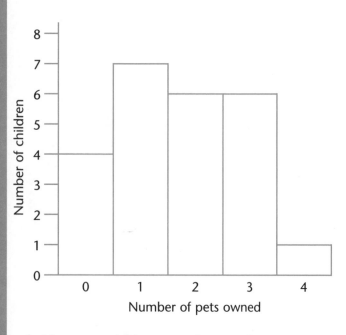

1. How many children owned one pet?
2. How many children owned three pets?
3. How many children owned two or more pets?
4. How many children owned less than two pets?
5. How many children are there in Timber-Wolf class?
6. What was the most number of pets owned by any of the children?
7. What was the most common (mode) number of pets owned?
8. How many children owned one or no pets at all?
9. What is the total number of children owning two or three pets?
10. One child owned four pets. True or false?

Training Tips

Think clearly and work step-by-step.

You can always use a rough piece of paper to make jottings, tally information or draw rough charts.

Frequency bar charts

Frequency charts may have grouped data.
This makes the data easier to handle.

Silver

Here is a frequency bar chart showing the number of questions answered correctly in the school 'Pop Quiz'.

1. How many children scored between 11 and 15 marks?
2. How many children scored between 0 and 5 marks?
3. How many children scored more than 20 marks?
4. How many children scored more than 10 marks?
5. How many children scored less than 11 marks?
6. What was the most common score in the pop quiz?
7. What was the maximum number of marks you could score?
8. What was the least common score in the quiz?
9. How many children scored more than 50%?
10. How many children took part in the pop quiz?

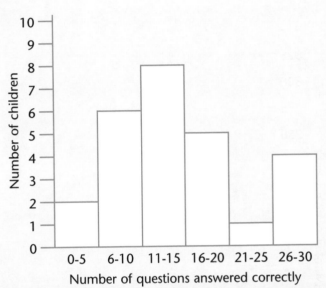

Gold

Look at the frequency bar chart in the Silver Medal question above.
The children did the same quiz again a week later during a wet lunchtime.
Their scores improved! Here are their scores.

Amy – 29	Jamal – 26	Sally – 25
Benny -27	Kirsty – 18	Tyrone – 13
Callum – 19	Logan – 30	Una – 8
Deniece – 20	Mimi – 28	Vinny – 6
Elizabeth – 22	Nell – 10	Will – 23
Fran – 14	Oprah – 11	Xavier – 11
Gareth – 9	Pierce – 17	Yunis – 24
Harry – 21	Quentin – 1	Zachary – 29
Isobelle – 21	Ricardo – 25	

Group the data in the same way and redraw the bar chart.
What differences do you notice between the two charts?

Line graphs

A graph with time on the x axis and numbers on the y axis is often shown with a line.
Sometimes the graph will show a set of points joined together by a line.
This shows how something is changing over a period of time.

This line graph shows the monthly sales of 'Spray-Rider' surf boards.

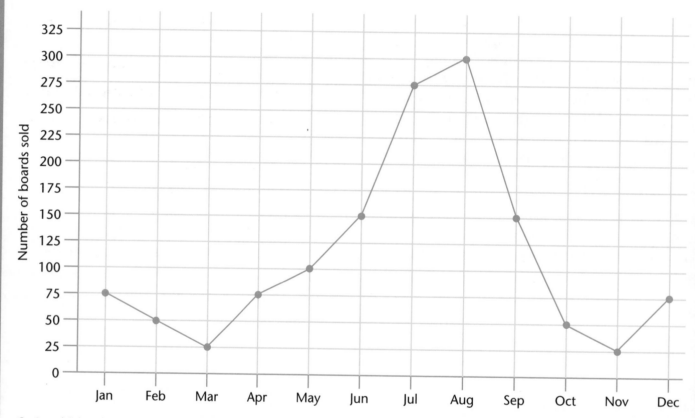

1. In which month were most boards sold?

2. How many surf boards were sold in April?

3. Between which two months did sales first start to rise?

4. Which month do you think Spray-Rider boards were offered with a 75% discount?

5. How many more boards were sold in September than December?

6. Why might there have been more sales in December than November?

7. How many boards were sold in September, October and November?

8. What percentage of the total sales were made in August? *(use a calculator)*

9. What is the total of boards sold in January, June and August?

Training Tips

When reading graphs, go *up* from the x axis first to meet the line, and then read *across* from the y axis to read the *value*.

Line graphs

Silver

This line graph is useful for converting miles to kilometres and vice versa.

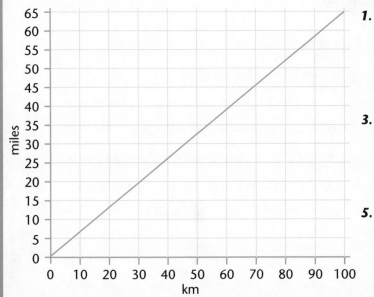

miles (y-axis: 0, 5, 10, 15, 20, 25, 30, 35, 40, 45, 50, 55, 60, 65)

km (x-axis: 0, 10, 20, 30, 40, 50, 60, 70, 80, 90, 100)

Using the line graph, change these road signs from km to miles or miles to km.

1.

Brighton	20 miles
Lewes	15 miles
Eastbourne	5 miles

2.

Bromley	35 miles
Central London	25 miles
Ashford	15 miles

3.

Manchester	40 km
Worsley	35 km
Chadderton	20 km

4.

Newcastle	50 km
Sunderland	18 km
Durham	4 km

5.

Birmingham	45 miles
Solihull	45 km
Worcester	85 km

Gold

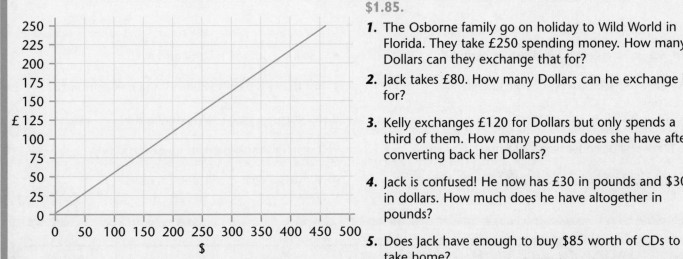

£ (y-axis: 0, 25, 50, 75, 100, 125, 150, 175, 200, 225, 250)

$ (x-axis: 0, 50, 100, 150, 200, 250, 300, 350, 400, 450, 500)

The tourist rate for the USA is one pound to $1.85.

1. The Osborne family go on holiday to Wild World in Florida. They take £250 spending money. How many Dollars can they exchange that for?

2. Jack takes £80. How many Dollars can he exchange it for?

3. Kelly exchanges £120 for Dollars but only spends a third of them. How many pounds does she have after converting back her Dollars?

4. Jack is confused! He now has £30 in pounds and $30 in dollars. How much does he have altogether in pounds?

5. Does Jack have enough to buy $85 worth of CDs to take home?

6. On the flight home Sharon buys perfume for $40 but pays with pounds. How many pounds does she need?

Probability

Probability is all about how likely something is to happen.
There are different ways of showing this.

a) Match one of these words to each of the statements below.

CERTAIN   LIKELY   UNLIKELY   IMPOSSIBLE

1. The next Olympics will be held in July 1967.

2. The sun will rise tomorrow.

3. Next Easter will be in April.

4. Tomorrow I will go outside during breaktime.

5. I will sit at the same table in class tomorrow.

6. Great Britain will win a medal at the next Olympics.

7. It will snow next Valentine's day.

8. School will close 2 hours early today.

9. If I toss a coin it will land on heads or tails.

10. I will grow 2 metres tonight.

b) Draw this probability line in your book.
Place these statements where you think they should appear on the line.

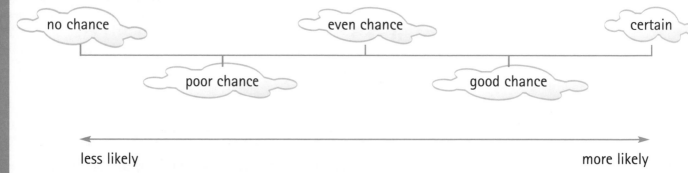

1. I will grow an extra head before bedtime.

2. Henry VIII will take part in 'Blind Date'.

3. The sun will set this evening.

4. There will be snow next Christmas.

5. Great Britain will win 50 Gold Medals at the next Olympics.

6. I will go outside next Saturday.

7. If I throw a dice it will land on an even number.

8. If I throw a dice it will land on a 5.

9. I will finish this page of questions today.

10. If I toss a coin it will land on heads.

Training Tips

When you roll a dice, there is an *equal* chance of rolling any of the numbers.

However many times you toss a coin, there is still an *even* chance of getting tails.

Probability

Silver

Draw this probability scale in your book.

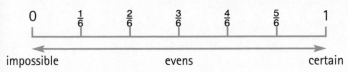

a) Charlie is rolling a 1 to 6 dice. Place each of these events on the scale using an arrow.

1. Charlie rolls an odd number
2. Charlie rolls a number greater than 4
3. He rolls a 7
4. He rolls a 6
5. Charlie rolls an even number
6. Charlie rolls a number between 3 and 6

b) There are 24 beads placed in a bag. 8 are red, 4 are blue, 6 are green and the rest are yellow. Charlie picks a bead. Draw a probability scale in your book. Place these statements on the scale.

1. The next bead Charlie picks will be blue
2. The next bead picked from the bag will be purple
3. The next bead picked by Charlie will be yellow
4. The next bead Charlie picks will be green

c) Charlie now gets rid of the yellow beads. What are the chances of these events happening? Use a fraction in your answer.

1. The next bead Charlie picks will be blue
2. The next bead picked from the bag will be yellow
3. The next bead picked by Charlie will be red
4. The next bead Charlie picks will be green

Gold

impossible		even chance		certain
0%	25%	50%	75%	100%
0	0.25	0.5	0.75	1
0	$\frac{1}{4}$	$\frac{1}{2}$	$\frac{3}{4}$	1

Use the grid above to help you to answer these by writing a fraction, a decimal or a percentage. Remember the answers may be between those numbers in the grid!

1. I am thinking of a certain day of the week. What chance is there that you could guess the day I'm thinking of? Write your answer as a fraction.

2. I have 4 playing cards face down on a table. One of them is the ace of spades. What is the chance of you picking the ace of spades? Write your answer as a percentage.

3. There are 8 beads in a bag. Four are yellow, three are blue and one is red. What is the chance that I would pick out a blue bead? Write your answer as a fraction.

4. There are 10 cards on a table, four tens, four queens and two kings. What is the chance that you would pick a queen? Write your answer as a decimal.

5. A football match ends 1–0 after 90 minutes. What chance is there that the goal was scored between 50 and 55 minutes? Answer with a percentage.

6. I have 100 coins. 30 are 1ps, 60 are 2ps and 10 are 5ps. What is the chance of me picking a 5p coin out from a bag? Write your answer as a decimal.

7. A sprinter takes 50 strides to complete the 100m. What chance is there that he steps on the 10 metre mark?

Finding the mean and the median

The **mean** is the average of a group of numbers. To find the mean – add all the amounts and divide by the number of amounts.

Example
19, 21, 23, 22, 24, 22, 23
Mean
= (19 + 21 + 23 + 22 + 24 + 22 + 23) ÷ 7
= 154 ÷ 7 = 22

The **median** is the middle number in a group of numbers. To find the median – put the numbers in order from smallest to largest and find the middle number.

Example
234, 345, 404, 222, 304, 411, 208
Median = 208, 222, 234, 304, 345, 404, 411
= 304 (the middle number)

Bronze

a) Find the mean of these sets of scores:

1. 11, 19, 20, 14, 18, 25, 26, 19, 19
2. 5, 16, 18, 20, 14, 11, 23, 16, 12
3. 32, 40, 39, 36, 38, 29, 31, 28, 33
4. 58, 55, 51, 48, 55, 48, 50, 51, 52
5. 101, 129, 112, 106, 127, 119, 117, 128, 123

b) Find the median of these numbers:

1. 349, 330, 321, 333, 401, 379, 345
2. 789, 777, 703, 693, 715, 733, 736
3. 253, 255, 257, 238, 239, 244, 254
4. 218, 299, 204, 257, 259, 226, 245
5. 1029, 1172, 1293, 1432, 1169

Silver

a) Find the mean of these sets of scores:

1. 121, 189, 184, 230, 164, 148, 215, 236, 169
2. 563, 416, 538, 480, 503, 434, 398, 546, 449
3. 732, 640, 568, 775, 652, 619, 756, 599, 662
4. 518, 515, 516, 517, 515, 518, 509, 514, 513
5. 1101, 1129, 1312, 1406, 1227, 1319, 1417, 1628, 1314

b) Find the median of these numbers:

1. 3490, 2330, 4301, 3578, 4008, 3278, 4113
2. 6783, 7977, 7603, 6953, 7815, 6733, 6736
3. 4203, 4456, 4702, 4103, 5541, 4491, 4493
4. 8019, 8434, 8839, 8644, 8593, 8238, 8426
5. 18229, 17172, 12493, 16994, 16991

Gold

a) Find the mean of these sets of scores:

1. 970, 919, 904, 999, 954, 938, 993, 956, 953
2. 1393, 1334, 1367, 1388, 1321, 1357
3. 3732, 3240, 3567, 3379, 3210, 3422
4. 6102, 6220, 6266, 6319, 6442, 6247
5. 9999, 10001, 11001, 10199, 12039, 19019

b) Find the median of these numbers:

1. 8930, 8892, 8789, 8834, 8821
2. 9012, 9220, 9326, 9245, 9222
3. 11011, 11101, 11111, 11110, 11012
4. 9999, 9989, 9909, 9899, 9809
5. 22022, 22222, 20220, 22002, 22202

Training Tips

Median is the middle (or medium) number.

Don't be MEAN, share your sweets equally!

Finding the mode

The mode is the most common value in a group of numbers. To find the mode – sort the numbers into sets of the same amount. Look for the set with the most numbers.

Example
23, 24, 22, 25, 23, 21, 26, 21, 22, 23
Group the numbers

21	22	23	24	25	26
21	22	23			
		23			

23 is the mode of this set

Bronze

Find the mode of these sets of scores:

1. 32, 33, 34, 35, 32, 33, 32, 33, 32, 36, 36

2. 21, 20, 21, 19, 22, 20, 21, 19, 20, 21, 25

3. 45, 44, 43, 40, 40, 43, 44, 45, 43, 40, 43

4. 76, 75, 77, 75, 79, 75, 76, 75, 78, 75, 76

5. 55, 55, 55, 54, 53, 54, 53, 54, 54, 55, 54

6. 101, 110, 101, 111, 111, 100, 110, 101, 109

7. 210, 212, 210, 211, 211, 212, 213, 212, 213

8. 222, 202, 220, 210, 211, 202, 202, 211, 221

9. 420, 420, 412, 410, 413, 423, 412, 440, 412

10. 999, 901, 990, 989, 901, 990, 989, 990, 999

Silver

a) Find the mode of these sets of numbers:

1. 480, 481, 488, 481, 483, 483, 488, 480, 481, 482

2. 326, 335, 363, 330, 324, 326, 337, 338, 364, 331

3. 101, 111, 100, 101, 111, 101, 100, 110, 111, 101

4. 455, 454, 454, 444, 455, 454, 455, 444, 455, 444

5. 11011, 11010, 11111, 11101, 11010, 11110, 11112

b) Create a set of six numbers that could produce these modes. Try to make them really difficult to answer.

1. 68

2. 101

3. 989

4. 325

5. 3

Gold

a) Find the mode of these sets of numbers:

1. 1, 1, 2, 2, 1, 2, 1, 2, 1, 2, 2, 1, 1, 2, 2

2. 3, 3, 4, 4, 5, 5, 3, 4, 5, 2, 4, 5, 3, 3, 2

3. 934, 923, 922, 934, 903, 933, 935, 923, 934, 993

4. 805, 819, 813, 812, 805, 814, 804, 804, 803, 805

5. 10001, 10002, 11002, 10002, 10003, 10010, 10100

b) Create a set of eight numbers that could produce these modes. Try to make them really difficult to answer.

1. 5

2. 110

3. 999

4. 10001

5. 100101

Training Tips

 Mode is the Most Common Value.

 Always write out the numbers again and sort them. Tick each number off so you don't miss any!

Finding the range

The range is the difference between the greatest and the least in a set of data.
Here are the scores out of 100 for the contestants in an archery contest.

> 52, 77, 21, 44, 86, 86, 62, 39, 95
> The range is 74. (95 – 21 = 74)

Bronze

a) **Find the range of these test results out of a hundred:**

1. 76, 34, 78, 54, 25, 26, 28, 47, 46, 78, 88

2. 22, 56, 76, 88, 89, 99, 15, 33, 75, 59, 78

3. 45, 67, 89, 37, 76, 75, 77, 90, 64, 66, 63,

4. 22, 26, 28, 19, 34, 67, 15, 77, 46, 54, 33

5. 52, 65, 63, 64, 91, 93, 95, 92, 53, 55, 96

b) **Find the range of these darts scores:**

1. 120, 100, 101, 86, 50, 75, 65, 160, 39, 77

2. 177, 105, 115, 164, 146, 111, 180, 96, 102

3. 56, 65, 64, 67, 59, 112, 77, 106, 108, 82

4. 90, 96, 67, 71, 81, 120, 115, 164, 119, 80

5. 134, 138, 112, 145, 167, 177, 120, 99, 97

Silver

a) **Find the range of these computer game scores out of a thousand:**

1. 849, 576, 386, 251, 693, 779

2. 624, 235, 907, 451, 356, 156

3. 354, 785, 651, 951, 357, 627

4. 156, 123, 145, 167, 841, 354

5. 621, 741, 639, 851, 906, 672

b) **Now find the range of these scores:**

1. 1250, 1425, 986, 674, 1402, 1328

2. 845, 867, 1249, 1167, 1346, 1406

3. 964, 1256, 826, 1460, 1239, 1488

4. 674, 539, 783, 485, 1351, 1029

5. 1451, 1324, 1480, 1369, 1378

Gold

a) **Find the range of these theme park attendance figures:**

1. 6783, 5493, 4463, 6745, 3459

2. 3267, 1567, 3654, 1289, 4587

3. 3265, 1266, 6537, 9514, 3647

4. 3645, 1259, 3665, 6034, 6154

5. 3975, 8861, 3245, 6816, 3056

b) **Now find the range of these football attendances:**

1. 9687, 8006, 6779, 7126, 7764

2. 9015, 6648, 7086, 7916, 9267,

3. 9035, 8776, 6716, 6325, 8415,

4. 6297, 9167, 9930, 8149, 8836,

5. 7168, 6015, 5419, 6617, 7766

Training Tips

It can help if you write the numbers down again in order of size.